HOTSPOTS
FUERTEV

C000062809

Written by Jill Benjamin and updated by Marcus Hardy, with additional research by Jenni Rainford

Published by Thomas Cook Publishing
A division of Thomas Cook Tour Operations Limited.
Company registration no. 1450464 England
The Thomas Cook Business Park, Unit 9, Coningsby Road,
Peterborough PE3 8SB, United Kingdom
Email: books@thomascook.com, Tel: + 44 (0) 1733 416477
www.thomascookpublishing.com

Produced by Cambridge Publishing Management Limited
Burr Elm Court, Main Street, Caldecote CB23 7NU

ISBN: 978-1-84157-855-2

First edition © 2006 Thomas Cook Publishing
This second edition © 2008
Text © Thomas Cook Publishing,
Maps © Thomas Cook Publishing/PCGraphics (UK) Limited

Series Editor: Linda Bass
Production/DTP: Steven Collins

Printed and bound in Spain by GraphyCems

Front cover photography © Thomas Cook

CONTENTS

WHAT'S IN YOUR GUIDEBOOK?

Independent authors Impartial, up-to-date information from our travel experts who meticulously source local knowledge.

Experience Thomas Cook's 165 years in the travel industry and guidebook publishing enriches every word with expertise you can trust.

Travel know-how Contributions by thousands of staff around the globe, each one living and breathing travel.

Editors Travel-publishing professionals, pulling everything together to craft a perfect blend of words, pictures, maps and design.

You, the traveller We deliver a practical, no-nonsense approach to information, geared to how you really use it.

● *The church at Betancuria*

INTRODUCTION
Getting to know Fuerteventura

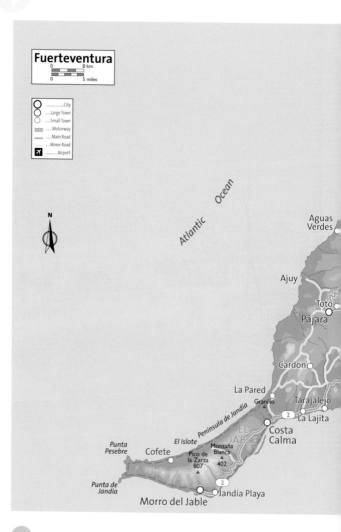

Fuerteventura

| 0 | 8 km |
| 0 | 5 miles |

○ City
○ Large Town
○ Small Town
▬ Motorway
▬ Main Road
▬ Minor Road
✈ Airport

N

Atlantic Ocean

Aguas Verdes

Ajuy

Toto

Pájara

Cardón

La Pared

Granillo

Tarajalejo

La Lajita

Costa Calma

Península de Jandía

Punta Pesebre

El Islote

EL JABLE

Cofete

Pico de la Zarza 807

Montaña Blanca 402

Punta de Jandía

Morro del Jable

Jandía Playa

Getting to know Fuerteventura

Fuerteventura is the second largest of the seven main Canary Islands, with a distance of about 100 km (60 miles) between Punta de la Tuñosa in the north and Punta de Jandía in the south. Despite this, it is comparatively sparsely populated, with a population of around 80,000 people.

It is generally said to be the oldest of the Canaries, mostly of basaltic origin, and as with all the other islands it has a unique landscape not found anywhere else in Europe. There is sunshine all the year round and a sea temperature of between 17°C and 23°C (63°F and 73°F). This island has very little rainfall and the water is supplied by coastal desalination plants. Fuerteventura lies 100 km (60 miles) from the coast of northwest Africa, and is between 30 and 40 minutes by car/passenger ferry from the neighbouring island of Lanzarote.

HISTORY

It is thought that the Majos were the original inhabitants of the island, believed to have come from North Africa. However, there continues to be much speculation between the experts about the accuracy of this. The people of the island both past and present are known as Majoreros (MaHorAIRos); this word literally means 'people of goatskin shoes' although not too many of the modern-day inhabitants wear them!

In 1402 the island was conquered by Jean de Bethencourt and Gadifer de la Salle for the crown of Spain, landing on the sands near the little village of Ajuy. The present village of Betancuria was named and founded by them, becoming the first capital of the island, until 1834. The current capital is Puerto del Rosario, a typically Spanish town that has a thriving and developing port.

ISLAND DEVELOPMENT

The big attractions of Fuerteventura are the year-round sunshine, the wonderful beaches, the spaciousness and the relaxing atmosphere. Tourism did not really develop until the 1970s, when people discovered the beauty of this desert-like island and its varying colours, ranging from the white sandy beaches to the gold of the dunes and the terracotta hues of the volcanic mountain ranges. Add to these the sudden surprises of lush green oases tucked between the hills, the astonishing turquoise of the surrounding seas, which are crystal clear, and the blue skies – and all of this is only four hours away from the UK.

Do not be surprised to come across hundreds of goats miraculously finding sustenance from the barren land. Goat's cheese is the second-largest sector of the economy on the island, tourism being the first.

The island government (the *Cabildo*) was formed in 1912, and in 1927 the seven main islands were separated into two provinces. Fuerteventura and Lanzarote are administered by Gran Canaria, while La Gomera, El Hierro and La Palma are under the wing of Tenerife. The whole group is under overall control of mainland Spain, which islanders refer to as 'the peninsula'. There is a strong feeling among the islanders as a whole that they would like to be free from Spanish control and be able to decide their own destiny. A couple of attempts have been made for total autonomy, but these were refused by the Spanish government on the grounds that the islands are not yet economically strong enough. There was indeed a time when the islands of Fuerteventura and Lanzarote were poor due to lack of rainfall, but things are now very different with the advent of tourism.

Many starving inhabitants from those difficult days uprooted their families and took ship to seek a better life, heading for Spanish-speaking countries such as Cuba and Venezuela. Scores of them perished on the way. The ones who managed to establish themselves abroad forged ties with the 'old country' that endure today.

You may wonder why there are still so many ruined *fincas* across the island landscape. The reason for this is that Spanish law stated that, when parents died, all property reverted to their children. Problems arose when family members who had left the island could not be traced, either perishing on the journey or just simply vanishing; to dispose of a property, all siblings have to agree to the sale.

THE BEST OF FUERTEVENTURA

With its unusual landscape and year-round sunshine, your stay on
Fuerteventura can be as relaxing or activity-packed as you like.

TOP 10 ATTRACTIONS

- **Watersports** No trip to this island would be complete without
  sampling at least one of the multitude of water-based activities
  on offer (see pages 17–22, 37, 43, 47, 51).

- **El Toston** Stunning fortified tower overlooking the harbour
  (see page 25).

- **Parque Natural de Las Dunas (Dunes National Park)** Europe's very
  own Sahara (see page 16).

- **La Oliva** A noteworthy town filled with 18th-century architecture
  (see page 54).

- **Baku** Fun-filled family entertainment complex, jam-packed with leisure, sports and entertainment (see page 17).

- **Jandía Peninsula** Mountains, nature reserve, plateaus, plains and stunning beaches. Enough said (see page 76).

- **Vega de Río Palmas (Valley of Palms)** Check out the island's long-kept secret (see page 63).

- **Nuestra Señora de la Regla (Pájara Parish Church)** Discover the Aztec-influenced design for yourself (see page 62).

- **Isla de los Lobos** A nature reserve with a plethora of beautiful wildlife to explore (see page 82).

- **Tiscamanita** Mill around here to enjoy the host of windmills that once ground the grain for the island's staple food. A Windmill Centre lies just outside this pretty village (see page 66).

◗ *Corralejo's coastline, seen from the air*

SYMBOLS KEY

The following symbols are used throughout this book:

ⓐ address ☎ telephone ☎ fax ⓦ website address ⓔ email
🕐 opening times ❶ important

The following symbols are used on the maps:

ℹ️	information office	⭕	city
✉️	post office	⭕	large town
🛍️	shopping	○	small town
✈️	airport	◼️	POI (point of interest)
➕	hospital	▬	motorway
🛡️	police station	▬	main road
🚌	bus station	—	minor road
✝️	church		
❶	numbers denote featured cafés, restaurants & evening venues		

RESTAURANT CATEGORIES

The symbol after the name of each restaurant listed in this guide
indicates the price of a typical two-course meal without drinks for
one person.

£ up to €10   ££ €10–20   £££ above €20

❱ *Pale golden sands at Costa Calma*

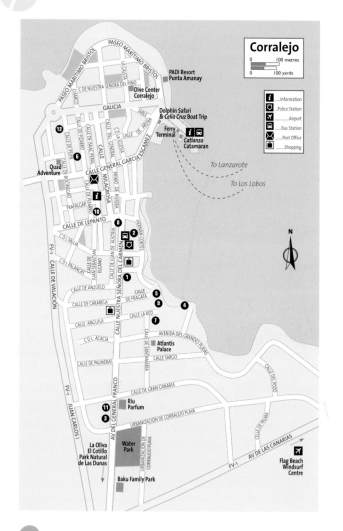

Corralejo

0 ___ 100 metres
0 ___ 100 yards

i .....Information
⊕ .....Police Station
✈ .....Airport
🚌 .....Bus Station
✉ .....Post Office
🛍 .....Shopping

PASEO MARÍTIMO BRISTOL
PASEO MARÍTIMO BRISTOL
PASEO MARÍTIMO BRISTOL
LA CALETA
CHARCO
C DE NUESTRA SEÑORA DEL PINO

PADI Resort
Punta Amanay

Dive Center
Corralejo

GALICIA

Dolphin Safari
& Celia Cruz Boat Trip

CALLE DE ARENA
JABLE
CALLE DE LA IGLESIA
CALLE DE ISAAC PERAL

Ferry
Terminal

Catlanza
Catamaran

CALLE DE PEDRO
CALLE DE PIZARRO
CALLE DEL CREBEJO
CALLE DEL PINO

12

6

Quad
Adventure

CALLE DE BOCINEGRO

CALLE GENERAL GARCÍA ESCÁMEZ

MILAGROSA
PRIMO DE RIVERA

TRAFALGAR

i

10

CALLE DE PIZARRO

CALLE DE LEPANTO

8

CALLE DE JUAN DE AUSTRIA

2

1

To Lanzarote

To Los Lobos

HERMANOS CORTÉS

N

C.D.I TALUA

C.D.L PALANGRE

CALLE DE JUAN
SEBASTIÁN ELCANO

CALLE DE ANZUELO

CALLE DE CARABELA

CALLE ANGUILA

C.D.L. ACACIA

CALLE DE PALMERAS

FV-1
CALLE DE VALACIÓN

CALLE NUESTRA SEÑORA DEL CARMEN

CALLE
DE FRAGATA

5
9

CALLE LA RED

7

4

AVENIDA DES GRANDES PLAYAS

CALLE DE SANTAMARÍA

Atlantis
Palace

CALLE SARGO

CALLE DE GRAN CANARIA

CALLE DEL POZO

Riu
Parfum

11

3

URBANIZACIÓN DE CORRALEJO PLAYA

URBANIZACIÓN DE CORRALEJO PLAYA

AV DEL GENERAL FRANCO

JUAN CARLOS I

La Oliva
El Cotillo
Park Natural
de las Dunas

Water
Park

Baku Family Park

CALLE DE PALMA

AV DE LAS CANARIAS

FV-1

✈
Flag Beach
Windsurf
Centre

Corralejo

Corralejo is one of the busiest of Fuerteventura's old resorts, situated in the north of the island, with beautiful beaches and good facilities.

Like many of the resorts, Corralejo started life as a small, tranquil fishing village, with views from the little harbour across the sea to Lanzarote, the neighbouring island to the north. Having been hurled into the 21st century, it has become a busy, bustling town engulfed by tourism. Houses of many colours seem to spring up like mushrooms overnight. The nice thing is that each housing complex is totally different in design; they seem to be trying to outdo each other for individuality.

The main part of the town still has its old houses and winding alleyways, many of the former now converted to either restaurants or shops but still maintaining their character.

Around the **old harbour** there is an abundance of bars and eating places. To sit there with a drink in your hand, watching the world go by, is a delight.

The **ferry terminal** is also in this area, and there are little booths selling either scuba diving, fishing excursions, or trips in the glass-bottomed boat. You can book here for a trip to the island of **Los Lobos**, or a three-island tour, as well as the boat to **Lanzarote**. There is a café at the terminal, and there are toilet facilities as well.

Between the old harbour and the ferry terminal lies the **Tourist Office** ⓘ (0034) 928 866 235, in front of which is a large, impressive statue by Paco Curbelo, a sculptor who lives on Lanzarote. Inside the office there are leaflets in several languages, telling you what is on offer for your entertainment, and the staff are very helpful.

The coastal road/dirt track to **El Cotillo** is not too easy to find unless you know where to look. Opposite Corralejo's quay, and next to the bus station, there is a well-worn track; it's not a spectacular journey, but it will give you an idea of how Fuerteventura looked before all the development began.

You will find most of the shops are along the main street, including a large, impressive perfume store operated by **Riu Parfum**, where you can

🔺 *Sand dunes outside Corralejo*

buy every imaginable brand of fragrance. The street is a jumble of bars and cafés. Side streets lead down to the sea, some to rocky shoreline, others to lovely golden sandy beaches. Here you can hire sun beds, should you wish, and you will find eating places right on the sands.

If you continue up the main highway going in the direction of **La Oliva**, you will find on the left-hand side, just before the first big roundabout, a complex called **Baku**, which in the local Guanche language means a meeting point (Guanche is a name for the original inhabitants of the Canary Islands). A good place to spend the day, Baku is where Corralejo's markets are held.

Carry on further along the coast road signposted to Puerto del Rosario and you will come to the breathtaking **Parque Natural de Las Dunas**. This mini-Sahara lookalike is now a protected area. Be careful if you park your car off the road, as it is easy to get stuck in the shifting sands blown by the strong onshore winds. To help you enjoy the wonderful beaches of this area in comfort, there are semicircular windbreaks constructed of blocks of lava to protect you from the sea breezes.

THINGS TO SEE & DO

Baku Family Park

One day really isn't enough to get round all that there is to offer in this unique, mega family entertainment centre. You'll find eight computerised bowling alleys, billiard table, table football and other arcade-type amusements, all with bar, snack and toilet facilities. There is wheelchair access.

You will also find mini-golf, a driving range, a minipark for children, an aviary and reptile houses, a water park and an aquarium and seal show. There is also an internet café, medical centre, municipal conference hall and theatre. All this is beautifully landscaped with free entry to the gardens and surroundings. Thoroughly recommended. ⓐ Going by car, leave Corralejo on the road to La Oliva; go round the first big roundabout and double back on your tracks. Baku will be on your right ⓦ www.bakufuerteventura.com ⓛ Daily. See website for specific hours of each section

Bike hire

Quad Adventure Quad expeditions are offered every day at 16.00 for about two hours. Quad safaris are every day at 10.30 for about four-and-a-half hours. Quad special tours (quad experience needed) can be arranged by agreement. Take your own picnic. ⓐ Calle Bocinegro 17 ⓣ 928 866 552/660 099 694 ⓦ www.quadadventure.net

Boat trips

Catlanza **Luxury Catamaran** Take a family trip on the 22-m (72-ft) *Catlanza* catamaran, which leaves from Corralejo harbour and anchors just off the idyllic beaches of Papagayo in Lanzarote. Watch out for dolphins and whales on the way. Tuna or vegetarian pasta, salad, fresh bread and fruit are served on board, along with wine, beer, fruit juices, soft drinks and water (all included in the price).

Those interested in sailing can help the captain and crew to trim sails and even take the helm. There is also the opportunity to have a jet-ski ride or snorkel (equipment available on board), or just to swim in the clear warm water.

Also on offer is the *Catlanza* **Exclusive Gold** for adults only (16 years and over). This excursion also sails to the beaches of Papagayo, but with a reduced number of guests and champagne cocktails served throughout the day. ⓐ Leaves from Corralejo harbour ① 928 513 022 ⓦ www.catlanza.com (make your reservation online and get a 10–15 per cent discount) ⓛ Trips 10.00–13.00, 13.30–16.30 Fri & Sun (13.20 in June, July, Aug)

Dolphin Safari *Siña Maria* Anchor off Isla de los Lobos to snorkel, swim and enjoy a buffet with drinks (the price is all-inclusive). The same company also does deep-sea fishing trips. Beer and soft drinks are available on board. ⓐ Kiosk on Corralejo Quay ① 928 535 418/686 725 327 ⓛ 6 trips a day 08.00–14.00 Mon–Sat

Glass-bottomed *Celia Cruz* Catamaran This boat has various trips ranging in length from 1 hour to 5 hours. ① 639 140 014 ⓔ celiacruz@fuerteventura.net

- a cruise directly to Isla de los Lobos, where you can swim, departs at 10.00 and 12.00 daily (if you want to stay on Lobos for longer, you can wait until the last boat back, which leaves at 16.00)
- a mini cruise leaves at 13.00 daily (not Tues and Sat)
- a trip to Papagayo and Lobos leaves at 11.00 Tues and Sat (returning at 16.00)

Diving
Dive Center Corralejo The courses listed below include equipment, book, video, logbook and certificate. ⓐ Calle Señora del Pino 22 ① 928 535 906

⬤ *Take your pick from the many boat trips that depart from Corralejo harbour*

📧 buceodcc@divecentercorralejo.com 🕐 08.30–18.30 Mon–Sat, closed Sun

- **Discover scuba diving**: a short introductory course, with the option of an open-water dive at additional cost
- **Scuba diving**: a course resulting in a qualification to dive up to 12 m (39 ft) with an instructor. Consists of three hours of theory, three hours in the pool and two hours in the sea, over a period of three days
- **Open-water diving**: a longer course taking five days, with five hours of theory, five hours of pool practice and four hours in open water

PADI Resort Punta Amanay ❷ Calle el Pulpo 5 (behind the harbour)
📞 928 535 357/656 447 657

- **Beginners' course**: one hour of theory, one hour for a pool lesson, one open-water dive

- **Open-water diver course**: five hours of theory, five hours of pool lessons, four open water dives, certificate
- **Advanced and speciality (e.g. Nitrox) courses**: on request

Fishing

Pez Velero Trips for fishers and spectators. Bring your own food. Water, soft drinks, beer and wine are included in the price.
ⓐ Muelle Deportivo (the harbour) ☏ 928 866 173 ⏱ Trips Mon–Sat from approximately 08.30–14.00, closed Sun

Surfing

There are numerous surfing kiosks and offices in and around the quay so only some are listed here.

Ventura Surf Offers a beginners' course of approximately eight hours. Lesson includes wet suit and board. Also offers private lessons.
☏ 928 866 295 ⓦ www.ventura-surf.com ⏱ Daily

Island Boarders Beginners' courses: four hours, covers safety, paddling and standing techniques; 12 hours (over three days) includes board control, board design, equipment, history, water survival and theory on types of wave breaks. Intermediate course: must be able to stand on the board, as it is the aim to catch and ride the waves on this course. Equipment rental available from 1 to 14 days. ☏ 928 866 389
ⓦ www.islandboarderssurfschool.com

Flag Beach Windsurf Centre This company offers not only windsurfing, but wave and kite surfing. They hold BSA and IKO certificates.

> ### FIESTAS
> **5 January** Los Reyes
> **16 July** Nuestra Señora del Carmen

🔺 *Corralejo's picturesque bay*

Windsurf beginners' three-day course. Surf and kite surf beginners' courses (hotel transport included). Board rental also available.
ⓘ 928 866 389 🕐 09.00–19.00 (summer); 09.30–17.00 (winter)

Tennis
Atlantis Palace Tennis Court, racket and ball hire are all available.
ⓘ 928 536 050 🕐 Daily

🔺 *Fun in the sun on Corralejo beach*

TAKING A BREAK

There is an abundance of eating houses in Corralejo, especially in **Calle de la Iglesia**, a street with atmosphere near to the harbour and the Tourist Office in the old part of town. Here you will find a variety of restaurants to choose from. Here is a selection of restaurants in other parts of the town:

Chablis Wine Bar £ ❶ Serves English breakfast (09.00–14.00) and pub meals. ⓐ Calle Nuestra Señora del Carmen ❶ 928 535 844 ⏱ 08.45–15.00 & 19.00–late ❶ No food Wed morning and Sun evening

El Patio £ ❷ Long-standing, well-respected favourite, open since 1983, serving international cuisine. ⓐ Calle Hernán Cortés 16 ❶ 928 866 668 ⏱ 18.00–24.00

Picasso's British Restaurant £ ❸ They have a separate children's menu and serve a popular roast dinner on Wednesdays from 12.00 to 20.00. ⓐ Centro Comercial Atlantico, Avenida General Franco ❶ 628 794 518 ⏱ 09.30–14.30 Mon, 09.30–14.30, 18.30–21.30 Tues–Sat, 10.00–20.00 Sun

Beach Club Waikiki ££ ❹ Right on the beach front. ⓐ Next door to **Waikiki disco pub** ❶ 928 535 697 ⏱ 19.00–05.00; restaurant 10.00–23.00

Corinthia Restaurant ££ ❺ Children's menu, complimentary hors d'oeuvres and international cuisine. Terrace on the beach. ⓐ Playa de Corralejo – Calle Arístides Hernández Morán ❶ 928 866 105 ⏱ 08.00–23.00

Méson Jada ££ ❻ Serves a selection of at least 25 fresh tapas every day. Children's menu also available. ⓐ Pedestrian street off Calle de Pejin ❶ 928 537 838 ⏱ 09.00–23.00 Mon–Sat, closed Sun

Pizzeria Di Napoli ££ ❼ A busy Italian restaurant serving generous portions. Wheelchair access. ⓐ Calle la Red ☏ 928 535 145 ⏱ 13.00–23.00

Poco Loco Grill ££ ❽ Very popular restaurant. ⓐ Calle Nuestra Señora del Carmen ☏ 928 866 662 ⏱ 13.00–23.30

Restaurante la Terraza ££ ❾ The house speciality is steak. ⓐ Calle Arístides Hernández Morán ☏ 928 867 127 ⏱ 09.00–24.00

Taj Mahal ££ ❿ Children's menu, Indian drinks. Parties catered for. Lunch and dinner takeaway. ⓐ Calle Gerardo Estevez Martín ☏ 928 536 364 ⏱ 12.30–15.00, 18.00–24.00

El Toro Bravo ££ ⓫ Popular Mexican steak house using high-quality ingredients to create simple, hearty dishes. ⓐ Centro Comercial Atlantico, Avenida General Franco ☏ 928 537 127 ⏱ 11.00–23.30

Julius £££ ⓬ Nice, upmarket place serving tapas with plenty of fish dishes too. ⓐ Calle de Pejin 10 ☏ 928 537 765 ⏱ 08.30–00.30

El Cotillo

Small, charmingly old-fashioned and good for bathing and surfing, El Cotillo is a place in which to chill out and is still a comparatively unspoilt seaside village. It has some wonderful seafood restaurants and offers excellent accommodation, such as the complex of studio apartments on the beach called Cotillo Sunset.

Around the old harbour the area is traditional, with little roads, somewhat reminiscent of those in Cornish towns, which lead down to the sea. Looking out to sea is a beautiful sculpture of a lady by Paco Curbelo, and another of two fishermen with a boat. On the quayside are two restaurants with indoor and outdoor seating. The atmosphere is peaceful, with gentle waves lapping over the rocks. The beach is very stony, but the local children seem oblivious to this and swim happily in the sheltered bay.

West of the village there is a huge sweep of beach next to the aquamarine sea, and windsurfers flit across the water like dragonflies. To the east are some beautiful lagoons surrounded by rock pools and good beaches. It's a safe area for children and adults to swim, as it is protected from the rough seas. Here you will find several unusual-looking houses. Originally built illegally, somehow they have survived and are now quite old.

About 3 km (2 miles) out of the village, you will come across El Faro (or the lighthouse). The nearer you get to the lighthouse, the quieter the area becomes.

THINGS TO SEE & DO

El Toston

A visit to this fortified tower on the cliffs overlooking the harbour is a must. In the 15th century Jean de Bethencourt built a castle on these grounds to protect the little port from invaders. This fell into disrepair and the present tower was begun in 1700. Three iron cannons once defended the coast, and the tower could accommodate a garrison of 12 men.

⬣ *Sea view from El Cotillo*

Nowadays the tower is a centre for history and culture for islanders and visitors alike, hosting art exhibitions in conjunction with the Tourist Office.

El Cotillo was originally called El Toston, but was renamed in the middle of the last century.

☎ 928 866 235

FIESTAS
7 August San Martin de Porres
21 August Nuestra Señora del Buen Viaje

TAKING A BREAK

El Toston Bar & Restaurant £ A British-owned bar and restaurant, visitors from all over come to eat here. It overlooks the old harbour of El Cotillo. ⓐ Calle Muelle Los Pescadores 2 ☎ 928 538 489 ⏰ Food served all day from 09.30

La Marisma ££ Fresh fish and Canarian food. ⓐ Calle Santos Tomas, near the German bakery ☎ 928 538 543 ⏰ 12.00–23.00

La Vaca Azul ££ This is in a prime position with seating right on the water's edge, as well as inside. Under new, experienced ownership and with a chef who is well known in the area, it will undoubtedly quickly become *the* place to eat. ⓐ The old harbour ☎ 928 538 685 ⏰ 11.00–22.00 Tues–Sun, closed Mon

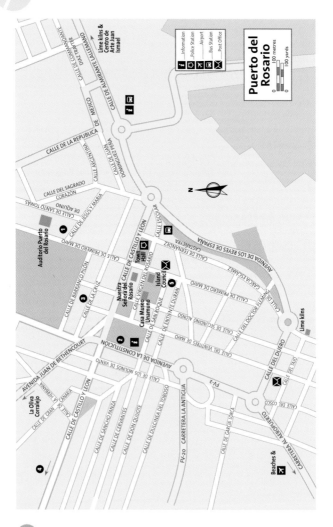

Puerto del Rosario

i	Information	
P	Police Station	
✈	Airport	
🚌	Bus Station	
✉	Post Office	

0 — 100 metres
0 — 100 yards

N

Lime Kilns & Centro de Arte Juan Ismael

CALLE DE COMMANDANTE DIAZ TRAYTER
CALLE DE ALMIRANTE LALLEMAND
CALLE DE MEJICO
CALLE DE LA REPUBLICA
CALLE DE JUAN DOMINGUEZ PEÑA
CALLE ARGENTINA
CALLE DEL SAGRADO CORAZON
CALLE DE AQUINO
CALLE DE JESÚS Y MARIA
CALLE DE SANTO TOMAS
CALLE ESCOLAR
CALLE DE PRIMERO DE MAYO
CALLE DE CASTILLO Y LEON
AVENIDA DE LOS REYES DE ESPAÑA
CALLE DE FERNANDEZ CASTAÑEYRA
GARCIA ESCAMEZ
CALLE DE BARRANCO PILON
CALLE DE LA CRUZ
CALLE VIRGEN DEL ROSARIO
CALLE DE S. ROQUE
CALLE DE ENTLLNTE DURAN
CALLE DE SECUNDINO ALONSO
CALLE DE PRIMERO DE MAYO
CALLE DEL DOCTOR FLEMING
CALLE DEL DUERO
CALLE DEL TAJO
Lime Kilns
AVENIDA JUAN DE BETHENCOURT
AVENIDA DE LA CONSTITUCION
CALLE DE LOS MOLINOS DE VIENTO
CALLE DE VEINTITRES DE MAYO
CALLE DE GRAN CANARIA
CALLE DE CASTILLO Y LEON
CALLE DE SANCHO PANZA
CALLE DE CERVANTES
CALLE DE LEON QUIXOTE
CALLE DE DULCINEA DEL TOBOSO
FV-20 CARRETERA LA ANTIGUA
CALLE DE GARCI LORCA
FV-2
CALLE DEL COSCO
CARRETERA AL AEROPUERTO

La Oliva Corralejo

Auditorio Puerto del Rosario ❶

Nuestra Señora del Rosario
Casa Museo Unamuno ❷
Town Hall
Island Council ❺
❸
❹ i
i

Beaches & ✈

Puerto del Rosario

Puerto del Rosario has been the capital of Fuerteventura since 1860. Previously called Puerto de Cabras (Goat's Port), it was renamed in 1957 to sound more appealing to tourists.

Puerto del Rosario is an important business, cultural and recreational centre. It is a sprawling, developing place, constantly growing and being modernised, with a thriving cargo and passenger harbour, and is only 5 km (3 miles) from the airport. Part of the harbour has recently undergone a transformation, offering souvenir shops, cafés and bars. Around the oldest part of the harbour, you will pass through narrow alleyways and quiet side streets, glimpsing the tops of trees and bushes behind garden walls.

Between 1975 and 1995 Puerto del Rosario was home to the Spanish Foreign Legion, transferred from Africa when Spain withdrew from the Spanish Sahara. Puerto del Rosario is great for those who love shopping and art. There is also a large church with, oddly, a licensed bar in its grounds!

⬤ *Harbour, Puerto del Rosario*

THINGS TO SEE & DO

Auditorio Puerto del Rosario

Concerts and dances. Tickets can be bought during the two hours beforehand at the box office, or you can reserve by telephone.
ⓐ Calle Ramiro de Maeztú 1 ☎ 928 532 186 ⏰ Events usually begin at 21.00

Casa Museo Unamuno

This was the hotel where the writer and philosopher Miguel de Unamuno lived in exile for some time, having spoken out about the dictatorship of Primo de Rivera in 1924.
ⓐ Calle Virgen del Rosario 11 ☎ 928 862 376 ⏰ 09.00–13.00 & 17.00–19.00 Mon–Fri, 10.00–13.00 Sat ❶ Admission free

Centro de Arte Juan Ismael

An arts centre which holds exhibitions of varying types.
ⓐ Calle Almirante Lallemand 30 ☎ 928 859 750 ⓦ www.cabildofuer.es
⏰ 10.00–13.00 & 17.00–21.00 Tues–Sat, closed Sun & Mon

Lime kilns (*hornos de cal*)

Along the coastal strip and on some access routes to the town are the remains of lime kilns, an industry lasting from the 17th century to the start of the 21st. Lime was exported to Gran Canaria, Tenerife and La Palma, and was used to paint houses and other buildings.

> **FIESTAS**
> **5 January** Los Tres Reyes
> **24 June** at El Matorral San Juan
> **29 June** at Guisguey San Pedro
> **4 August** at Tetir Santo Domingo de Guzman
> **7 October** Nuestra Señora del Rosario
> **30 November** at Tetir San Andres

Sculptures

The modern-day capital is especially proud of its sculptures, on display throughout the town. You will find them in pedestrianised areas, on roundabouts, squares and streets, even on the shore near the harbour. Involvement in this project has led to the holding of the annual international sculpture symposium, where sculptors create their works in public.

Tour by bus

There is a bus stop right next to the quay with departures every 45 minutes between 09.00 and 14.00. The bus carries a '*Vamos en Guagua Turista*' (Let's take the Tourist Bus) logo on the side.

TAKING A BREAK

Cazuela £ ❶ Pizzas, pastas and Canarian food. Friendly and inexpensive. ⓐ Calle Ramiro de Maeztú 5 ❶ 928 852 195 ❶ 08.00–19.00 Mon–Fri, 08.00–15.00 Sat, closed Sun

Chino Gran Mundo £ ❷ Clean, cheap and reliable. ⓐ Avenida de la Constitución 2 ❶ 928 859 304 ❶ 11.30–16.30, 19.30–24.00

Lola's Tapas £ ❸ Good-value tapas in a friendly atmosphere. ⓐ Calle de la Cruz 8

Ristorante Roma ££ ❹ Italian cuisine. ⓐ Calle Maria Estrada 33b ❶ 928 532 249 ❶ 12.00–23.00

La Saranda ££ ❺ This cute little eatery serves a variety of great tapas, freshly caught fish and a host of delicious seafood. ⓐ Primero de Mayo 46 ❶ 928 530 330 ❶ 08.00–17.00 Mon–Sat, closed Sun

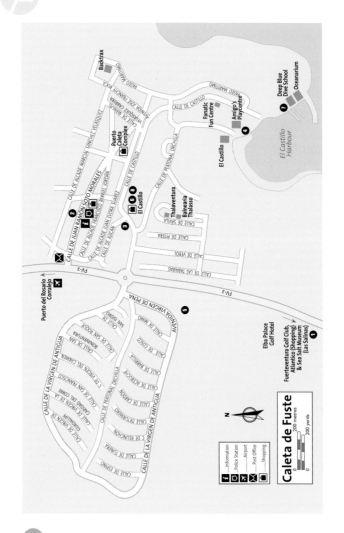

Backtrax

Deep Blue Dive School

Oceanarium

PASEO MARÍTIMO

PASEO MARÍTIMO

Calle de Manuel Velázquez Cabrera

Calle de José Franchy Roca

Avenida José Franchy Roca

Calle de Castillo

Fanatic Fun Centre

Amigo's Playcentre

El Castillo Harbour

Calle de Alcalde Marcial Sánchez Velázquez

Puerto Caleta Complex

El Castillo

Calle de Castillo

Calle de Pastoral Orchilla

Calle de Juan Ramón Soto Morales

Calle de Alcalde Juan Pidora Suárez

Calle de Alcalde Francisco Borrel Jordan

El Castillo

Thalaventura

Balnearia Thalasso

Calle de Juan

Calle de Savila

Calle de Pitera

Calle de Verol

Calle de las Trabajas

FV-2

FV-2

Puerto del Rosario
Corralejo

Avenida Virgen de Peña

Calle de Mimo

San Isidro

Calle de San Roque

Calle de San Buenaventura

Calle de San Francisco

Calle de la Virgen del Carmen

Calle de San Conде

Calle de Cosco

Calle de Barрил

Calle de Alcornoque

Calle de Cardón

Calle de Retamillo

Calle de Relinchón

Elba Palace Golf Hotel

Fuerteventura Golf Club, Atlántico (Shopping) & Sea Salt Museum (Las Salinas)

Calle de la Virgen de Antigua

Calle de San Andrés

Calle de Caridad del Conde

Calle de San Francisco

Calle de la Virgen de la

Calle de Gibraltar

Calle de Beliunción

Calle de la Virgen de Antigua

Calle de Yunda

Calle de Espino

Caleta de Fuste

Information
Police Station
Airport
Post Office
Shopping

0   200 metres
0   200 yards

N

Caleta de Fuste

This town is one of the main resorts. Located in the middle of the east coast, it is very convenient for the airport.

Caleta de Fuste is built around a horseshoe-shaped bay with a safe, sandy beach, so it is a good choice for holidaymakers with small children. You can surf (even as a beginner), dive, cycle, play tennis or squash, and take yachting trips with picnics or go deep-sea angling. Golf plays a big part in the district's entertainment.

El Castillo (the castle) was built in 1741 to defend the area from invaders and shows how important Caleta de Fuste was in the 18th century. Today it stands next to a harbour complex with restaurants, bars, watersports facilities and a supermarket. There are also many bars and restaurants in the centre of town around El Castillo Commercial Centre.

To travel to **Puerto del Rosario** by bus, take the no. 3, which leaves once an hour.

THINGS TO SEE & DO

Amigo's Playcentre

Many parents of small children fear they will find it difficult to participate in activities. However, Amigo's Playcentre is manned by qualified British staff and is for children up to six years of age. They have soft play areas, a separate baby area, arts and crafts, and cater for birthday parties, too.

🅐 By the Castillo San Jorge ApartHotel suites ❶ 669 914 838

🕒 10.00–21.00

Atlantico

This is a lively shopping and entertainment centre where you will find a six-screen cinema that shows Spanish-language films, 40 shops with some well-recognised names among them and a supermarket. There is a bowling centre with ten lanes, and many restaurants and snack bars. In addition, a bank is open all day, seven days a week.

⬥ *Blue sky over Caleta de Fuste's harbour*

ⓐ Across from the golf course on the main road out of Caleta de Fuste, towards Jandía ⓑ The cinema, bowling alley and restaurants remain open well into the early hours

Boat-based activities

Oceanarium *Explorer* The *Explorer* is a glass-bottomed submarine, and the activity takes 90 minutes. A guide describes the most common fish found in local waters, including a type of shark and stingrays, most of which can be seen in the Oceanarium. Some you can even feed or touch. There is also an octopus house and a real pirate boat. Finally, Harley the sea lion will emerge from the water and come on deck.

ⓐ The harbour ☎ 928 163 514 🕐 Ring for details of excursion times

Oceanarium Catamaran In the summer season, after a visit to the Oceanarium, you can take an afternoon trip on the island's biggest catamaran, which will take you on a search for marine life. Throughout the year, dolphins and whales are seen on an average of 40 per cent of the trips. The marine turtles of Pozo Negro are seen most days. You get a chance to snorkel or swim in Pozo Negro with yet more marine species.

ⓐ The harbour ☎ 928 160 149 🕐 Ring for details of excursion times

Golf

Fuerteventura Golf Club There is an 18 hole, par-70 golf course 4 km (2½ miles) from Caleta de Fuste and 8 km (5 miles) from the airport. Part of a 5-star hotel, it is also open to non-residents. It is predominantly flat except for the last two holes, and there are three lakes with a stream meandering through the course. Buggy paths connect all holes. It has a 50-bay driving range, large putting green and a second one for chipping and bunker shots. Professional tuition is available in various languages. Buggies, trolleys and two classes of clubs can be hired. There is a large pro shop in the main foyer of the hotel.

ⓐ Carretera de Jandía, 11 km ☎ 928 160 034 🖷 928 163 658

Elba Palace Golf Hotel The golf resort, with 5 stars, is set amidst a village of quality houses of differing designs. The hotel-cum-clubhouse has been built in the Canarian style of architecture, with beautiful traditional balconies. There is an attractive inner patio with palm trees, just the place to sit and relax after a strenuous round of golf. There are 61 en-suite bedrooms, all with air conditioning, mini-bar, satellite TV and a safe. There is a gymnasium, floodlit artificial grass paddle/tennis court, swimming pool for adults and a separate children's pool. The mature gardens are an excellent place in which to take a stroll away from the heat of the sun.

☎ 928 163 922/0044 (0)871 423 5051 🖷 928 163 923

Health and beauty

Balnearia Thalasso This wellness centre offers six pools, mud wrapping, massage, facial treatments and many more pampering options.
ⓐ Calle Sávila 2 ⓣ 928 160 961 ⓔ fuerteventuratalaso@ spabalnearia.com ⓛ 10.00–19.00

Thalaventura You will find a huge variety of beauty treatments here, including: massages, facials, thalassotherapy, waxing and hair removal. Specific body treatments include Aquagym and stretching (over 15 year-olds). Manicures, pedicures, eyebrow and eyelash tinting and a three-day anti-stress course are also available. There are indoor and outdoor pools, a geyser, bubble beds, water jets and jacuzzi.
ⓐ Calle Sávila 10 ⓛ 10.30–17.00 Mon–Sat; closed Sun

The Hire Shop

Stocks a good collection of things to hire, from mobility scooters to pushchairs and DVD players. Delivery and collection. Ring for information.
ⓣ 619 908 848 ⓦ www.the-hireshop.net

Motorbikes

Backtrax Off-road motorcycle tours for all levels of experience. Full kit plus food and drink are included.
ⓐ Local 1, Hotel Antigua Suites ⓣ 928 160 206 ⓦ www.backtrax1.com
ⓘ Full motorcycle licence required to ride

The Sea Salt Museum

Not far outside Caleta de Fuste, on the Jandía road, is **Las Salinas**, where the Sea Salt Museum is housed. You will find it difficult to miss, as there is a huge skeleton of a whale outside.

Sea salt was first collected in 1861 at Gran Tarajal. An area south of El Castillo soon followed, and in the 20th century Las Salinas del Carmen was started, along with various others dotted around the island, continuing production for a number of years, before falling into disuse due to competition from imported salt. Recently, however – as on the neighbouring island of Lanzarote – there has been a revival in the use of this naturally produced salt.

🕐 09.30–17.30 Tues–Fri, 09.30–17.50 Sun; closed Mon & Sat

Shopping

Caleta de Fuste has several shopping centres to explore. Many of these are lively by day, with a good mixture of shops, bars and restaurants; others come to life during the evening, and are the best places for nightlife. There is a large and impressive perfume store operated by **Riu Parfum** where you can buy every imaginable brand of fragrance available.

Tennis

El Castillo The same company also offers mini-golf, paddle tennis (a form of tennis popular in Spain) and basketball.

🅐 Barceló Complex (behind the main entrance to the Barceló Hotel, next to the beach)

Watersports

Fanatic Fun Centre Basic course, or advanced course of six hours.

🅐 El Castillo harbour 🅣 928 535 999 🕐 Daily

Deep Blue Dive School Beginners' introductory course of 3½ hours over three days or a three-full-day course ending with a PADI certificate.

🅐 El Castillo harbour 🅣 928 163 712 Ⓦ www.deep-blue-diving.com 🕐 Daily

TAKING A BREAK

Café Mozart £ ❶ Sells various coffees, home-made cakes and more. 🅐 Centro Comercial Atlantico, Loc. 28 🅣 928 163 254 🕐 09.30–22.30

🔺 *Caleta de Fuste's sandy beach is safe for children*

Syataki £ ② Traditional Greek food and Greek music. ⓐ Caleta Amigos shopping centre ① 928 163 613

El Camarote ££ ③ Reputedly the best fish restaurant in the area. ⓐ Muelle Deportivo s/n ① 928 869 073 ⓛ 12.00–22.30

La Frasquita ££ ④ Specialising in fresh fish, you can select from the catch of the day as it is brought to your table. ⓐ Peatonal Orchilla s/n ① 928 163 657 ⓛ 13.00–16.00, 18.00–22.00 Tues–Sun, closed Mon

Gambrinus ££ ⑤ Chain of seafood restaurants found all over Spain. ⓐ Centro Comercial Broncemar Beach Ajican 4 ① 928 163 555 ⓛ 10.00–24.00

Mexican Corner ££ ⑥ Mexican food. ⓐ Centro Comercial El Castillo ① 928 163 460 ⓛ 12.00–23.00

La Paella ££ ⑦ Local and international dishes. Watch the sun setting over the bay near the castle. ⓐ Plaza Ingeniero Liste ⓛ 12.30–22.00 ⓘ Wheelchair access

La Bodeguita ££ ⑧ Highly recommended Italian. Local produce, cooked and served in authentic Italian style. Excellent pizza, meat and fish dishes. ⓐ Centro Comercial El Castillo ① 928 163 277 ⓛ 12.30–late

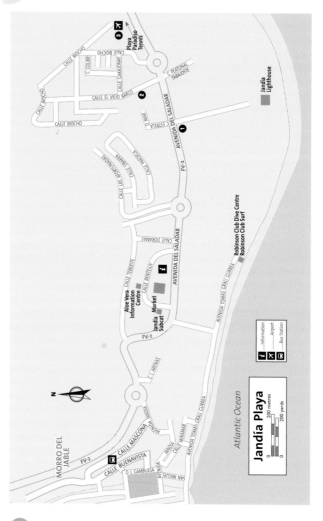

Jandía Playa

Jandía Playa

Jandía Playa is in the very south of Fuerteventura, 2 or 3 km (a couple of miles) to the east of Morro del Jable (see page 49). Its beach is a magnet for watersports enthusiasts. There are so many water activities on offer here that you can shop around for exactly what you want.

THINGS TO SEE & DO

Aloe Vera Information Centre
Visit the Aloe Vera Information Centre where you can learn more about the growing and processing of this locally produced plant, and sample some of the potions and lotions.
ⓐ Apartado de Correos 89 (just behind where the market is held on Avenida Saladar) ❶ 945 191 081 ⓔ Aloe-vera-canarias@web.de

Bikes
Fuertebike A telephone call is all that is needed for this excursion. Everyone is taken by car to visit Betancuria. The journey then continues by bike to the coastal village of Ajuy for a picnic on the beach. You are then transported up the hill and continue by bike to La Pared, a 10-km (6-mile) downhill run, from where you're driven back to your starting point (pick-up and set-down at Costa Calma too). Another trip is available for those who want a more challenging ride, plus some walking and cave exploration.
❶ 629 362 795 ❶ Mon, Wed, Thur, Fri & Sat

Boat-based activities
Charters Avanti An amazing experience of real sailing on a 26m (85 ft) yacht which took part in the Whitbread 'round the world' race. There are only three of these boats left in the world. You sail with a professional skipper who has two trips around the world under his belt. Children up to 12 years old go half price; second child goes free. Free bar for light alcoholic and soft drinks, sandwiches of local cheese and salad, plus fruit – all included in the price.
❶ 629 591 455 ❶ 10.30–14.30 Fri & Sat

⬥ *Watersports are very popular at Jandía Playa*

Jandía Subcat The trip takes approximately 90 minutes and the sub dives up to 30 m (100 ft) deep. You will see a myriad of different fish, both large and small, if you are lucky. ☎ 928 166 392/629 153 583 ⓦ www.subcat-fuerteventura.com ⓔ info@subcatfuerteventura.com ⏰ 09.00, 10.45, 12.30, 14.00, 16.00 Tues–Fri ❶ Admission charge for trip

Tennis
Playa Paradiso ☎ 928 541 060 ⏰ 08.00–20.00

Watersports
Robinson Club Dive Centre This reliable diving centre covers all levels of diving. Basic courses start every Sunday and Tuesday. Twice a week there is a children's course in the pool. Every diver needs a licence, log book, medical certificate and insurance. ☎ 928 541 065 ⓔ info@tauschule-fuerteventura.de ⏰ Diving tours with guides start every day at 09.00 & 14.00; night dives on Wed ❶ Minimum age for sea dives is 12

Robinson Club Surf Offers a beginners' surfing course lasting between 10 and 12 hours. Board rental is available. ☎ 928 169 539

TAKING A BREAK

Boot and Ball Sports Bar ££ ❶ English breakfast, jacket potatoes, hot and cold snacks, traditional Sunday roast from midday. Children's mini-cine. Big-screen TV with all major sports shown live. ⓐ Avenida del Saladar 17 ⏰ 10.30 onwards

Pizzeria Faro ££ ❷ Serves pizza, and meat and fish dishes. ⓐ Centro Comercial Faro Atlantica ☎ 928 540 534

Restaurant Marabu ££ ❸ A good Spanish restaurant, very popular with the locals. Serves both national and international dishes. ⓐ Calle Fuente de Hija ☎ 928 544 098

◌ *Blue skies at Costa Calma*

Costa Calma

This is a tranquil family resort on a huge sweep of pale golden sand backed by low cliffs. Elegant houses now mingle with hotels, apartments and commercial centres.

Of course, Costa Calma's fabulous beaches attract an abundance of watersports fans, and every July the area hosts the international windsurfing championships.

The commercial **Centro Sotavento** contains a good selection of restaurants and bars, which come to life in the evening.

On the seafront, part of the El Granillo housing scheme, is the Hotel Rio Calma. Opened in 2003, the hotel was designed by Basque architect Luis Sanchez. The beautiful colonial-style architecture is really eye-catching and everything is of the highest quality. Definitely one of the most impressive hotels on the island, with surprisingly reasonable prices, it offers everything you could wish for, from a wellness centre to swimming pools, tennis and squash courts, mini-golf and pitch-and-putt. There are conference rooms, an internet café, two restaurants and five bars. Nearly all of the 384 rooms overlook the sea, and they are all fully equipped. The gardens are well kept and peaceful – even if you don't stay there, it is worth going to see such an unusual and beautiful building.

Costa Calma has its own sea-water desalination plant, which was built in 1986 and provides many of the hotels and holiday complexes with water. In addition, waste water is piped to a sewage plant to be processed and re-used as *agua verde*. This recycled water helps to keep the gardens of hotels and complexes lush and green, and enables the avenues of beautiful palms and Canary pines to thrive.

A bus goes to Jandía and Morro del Jable, which are Costa Calma's neighbouring resorts. This runs hourly, on the half hour (🕑 09.30–21.00 Mon–Sat).

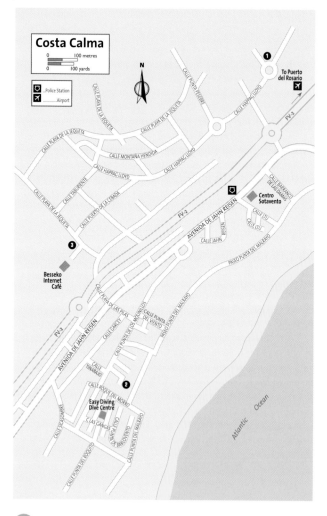

Costa Calma

0 — 100 metres
0 — 100 yards

🚓 ....Police Station
✈ ....Airport

N

To Puerto
del Rosario ✈

Besseko
Internet
Café

Centro
Sotavento

Easy Diving
Dive Centre

Atlantic Ocean

THINGS TO SEE & DO

Diving

Easy Diving Diving trips leaving the base at approximately 09.30 and return at approximately 13.00. There is also a flexible afternoon dive. Beginners' diving course over five days with about five hours of theory, two dives in the pool and four half-hour dives in open water. Snorkelling trips for adults and children are also offered.

ⓐ 200 m (220 yds) from Centro Comercial Botanico ⓣ 928 876 305
ⓛ 09.00–16.30 Mon–Sat, closed Sun

Internet café

Besseko ⓣ 928 876 420/620 484 447 ⓛ 10.00–24.00

TAKING A BREAK

Franco Italiano ££ ❶ Pizza and pasta. ⓐ Calle Cañada del Rio
ⓣ 928 875 371 ⓛ 18.00–23.00 Mon–Sat, 12.00–15.00 Sun

Galeria ££ ❷ German-run restaurant, serving a variety of Mediterranean food and pasta dishes. ⓐ Calle Risco Blanco s/n
ⓣ 928 875 416 ⓛ From 18.00 Tues–Sun, closed Mon

Restaurante Copa ££ ❸ German-owned with well-prepared food. Excellent service and children can draw on the paper tablecloths using crayons supplied by the owner. ⓐ Centro Comercial El Palmeral
ⓣ 646 755 305 ⓛ 18.00–22.00 Tues–Sun, closed Mon

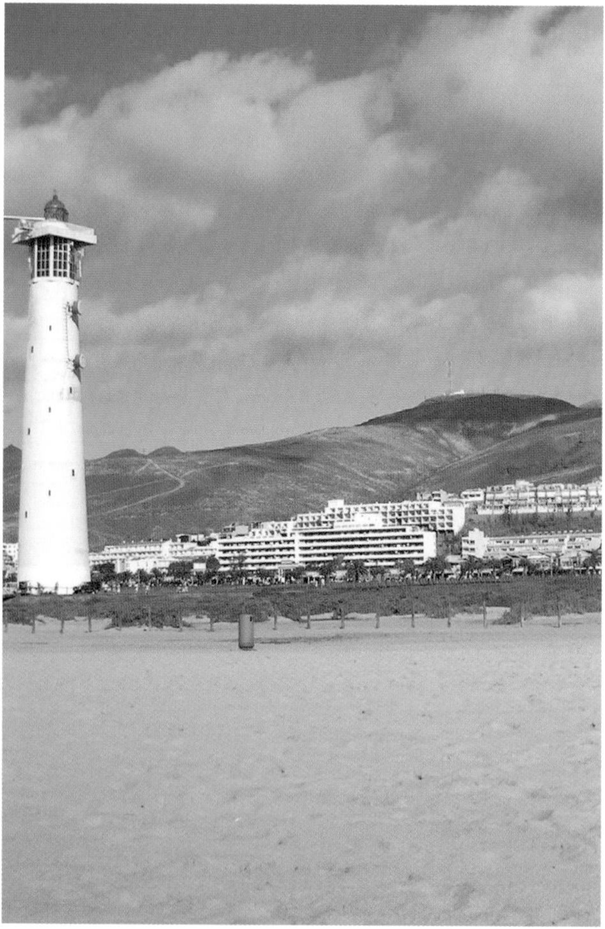

Jandía Playa at Morro del Jable

Morro del Jable

It is hard to believe that this was once another small fishing village, in what was a remote part of the island. Situated in the island's south, it has become one of the largest holiday centres on Fuerteventura. There is something for everyone: sea, beaches, hotels, apartments, commercial centres, restaurants, bars, shops and a marina.

The remains of the old village lie on the slopes of a *barranco* (a steep hillside), where the fishermen still go in and out of the harbour. The lighthouse situated on the **Punta del Matorral** marks the most southerly point of Fuerteventura. Inland, towards the mountains, there is the wild and unspoilt countryside of **northern Jandía**, a paradise on earth for walkers.

To the east of Morro del Jable lies the **Jandía Playa**, with the most breathtakingly beautiful fine, pale-golden sandy beaches bordering a stunning, crystal-clear turquoise sea (see page 41).

Much of the peninsula, with its rugged mountains, is a conservation area and forms part of the **Parque Natural de Jandía**. In some of the remote mountain valleys it is still possible to see wild goats and donkeys.

The longest beaches with the highest waves are to be found in Jandía, making it a must for surfers and windsurfers – winds here can reach up to Force 9! On the northwestern side of Jandía is the secluded beach of **Barlovento**, popular with scuba divers and naturists.

THINGS TO SEE & DO

Boat-based activities
Catamaran Magic This is run by a company that also operates in Ibiza and Gran Canaria. The trip includes a light meal of chicken, salad, potatoes and *mojo* (a spicy, typical Canarian sauce, see page 85), plus two drinks (water, soft drinks, beer and wine). The boat cruises along the coastline on the look-out for dolphins and other marine life.
☎ 699 470 522 **🕐** Trips daily from 10.30–14.00

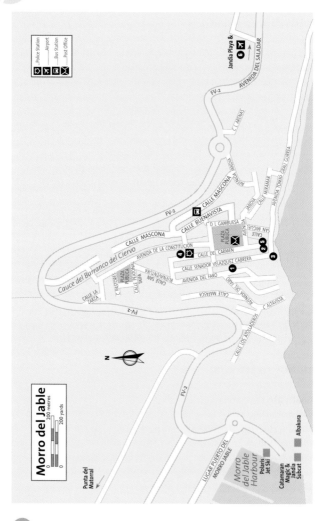

Morro del Jable

200 metres
200 yards

Punta del
Matorral

Jandia Playa &

Police Station
Airport
Bus Station
Post Office

Morro
del Jable
Harbour

Catamaran
Magic & Jandia
Subcat

Polaris
Jet Ski

Albakora

Polaris Jet Ski Sessions start every two hours from 08.00 to 18.00 and last for 90 minutes. Life jackets are supplied.
ⓐ In the harbour of Morro del Jable ❶ 616 437 184/639 706 930
🕒 Closed Sun

Fishing
Albakora Deep-sea fishing for a maximum of five people. Cheese and ham *bocadillos* (rolls), beer and soft drinks are available on board.
ⓐ Morro del Jable harbour 🕒 Daily trips, approximately 09.00–14.00

The Blue Nose Big-game fishing, food and drinks on board. ⓐ By the petrol station in the harbour ❶ 628 021 451 🕒 Daily trips 09.00–14.00

🔺 *Morro del Jable*

TAKING A BREAK

Refugio £ ❶   Cheap local bar with good tapas. ⓐ Calle Senador Velázquez Cabrera 3 ❶ 928 547 062

Restaurante Charly ££ ❷   This long-established restaurant always has good food, with fresh fish a speciality. ⓐ Plaza de Cirilo López (near the taxi rank) ❶ 928 541 066

Leos ££ ❸   Lovely atmosphere, and right by the sea – you can sit and watch the world go by. Family-run business serving good food, including fresh fish. ⓐ Avenida Marítima ❶ 928 540 724

Picola Italia ££ ❹   A really good Italian restaurant, with excellent pizza and pasta. ⓐ Nuestra Señora del Carmen 39 ❶ 928 541 258

Posada San Borondón ££ ❺   A characterful restaurant decorated as a ship, so you can't miss it! Serves mainly Spanish food, with *flambés* a speciality. Live music at the weekends adds to the atmosphere. ⓐ Plaza de Cirilo López ❶ 928 541 428 ❶ 18.00–02.00, closed Sun

Coronado £££ ❻   A sophisticated restaurant with a good ambience, a place to go for that special, romantic dinner. Excellent service, international cuisine. ⓐ Apartments Coronado, between the Riu Calypso and the Hotel Riu Palace ❶ 928 541 440 ❶ 17.30–24.00, closed Tues

❶ *Camels feel at home in the island's hot, arid climate*

Northern Fuerteventura

LAJARES

Just ten minutes' drive from Corralejo, this somewhat rambling village
is well worth a visit to watch the local women making their traditional
openwork embroidery. Exquisitely crafted, the finished items are for sale
in the shop marked **Artesanía de Lajares** where you can buy tablecloths,
napkins, shirts and aprons, together with other small embroidered items.
There are also many souvenirs for sale including some hand-painted
pottery. ◐ 09.00–19.00 Mon–Fri, 09.00–13.00 Sat, closed Sun

The village is also notable for its wrestling arena, in which the
traditional Lucha Canaria takes place.

If you're in need of a good meal, try **El Patio de Lajares**, a hotel
restaurant offering Spanish and German cuisine. ⓐ Calle la Cerea 9
ⓘ 650 134 030 ◐ Wed–Sun for lunch and dinner ❶ Reservations required

LA OLIVA

Sixteen kilometres (10 miles) south of Corralejo lies La Oliva, a part-old
part-new town, the centrepiece of which is the church of **Nuestra Señora
de la Candelaria** (Our Lady of Candelaria) (1711). An impressive building,
the church's white walls contrast starkly with the square bell tower built
of black volcanic stone.

On the outskirts of town there is a very interesting building called
La Casa de los Coroneles (The House of the Colonels), built at the
beginning of the 18th century for the military forces who wielded great
power at that time. It is a fortress-like manor house, with its wooden
balconies, doors and shutters decorated with carvings. Above the
entrance is the coat of arms of the Cabrera family, with a crown, a tree
and a goat. ◐ 09.00–14.00, 16.00–19.00 Tues–Sat, closed Sun & Mon

Close by is the **Centro de Arte Canario**, which was opened by Manuel
Delgado Camino. This gallery houses one of the finest collections
of contemporary Canarian art; beautifully displayed, the exhibitions of
well-known Canarian artists are changed each year. There are also some
permanent exhibitions, amongst which are the works of Alberto

Manrique. The mood is one of tranquillity as you walk through the centre's gardens to each gallery, past sculptures in stone and metal.
🅐 Casa Mané (between the church and the Casa de los Coroneles)
🏛 928 868 233 🕙 10.00–18.00 Mon–Sat (summer); 10.00–17.00 Mon–Sat (winter) ❶ Admission charge

TINDAYA

Driving south from La Oliva, the village of Tindaya lies at the base of **Montaña Tindaya**, from the peak of which on a clear day you can see across to Mount Teide, the highest mountain on Tenerife.

Because of its unusually light marble colour, Montaña Tindaya used to be regarded by the islanders as a religious place. They left behind a large number of outlines of feet carved into the rock which were said to keep away the evil spirits. On the drive from La Oliva or El Cotillo the almost white mountain stands out from the others of ochre and terracotta. Eduardo Chillida, a well-known Basque sculptor in the last century, wanted to hollow out the mountain, making it into a work of art in its own right.

In the village itself there is a *lucha* arena (*lucha* is Canarian wrestling, and is extremely popular), a rather lavishly appointed little church, a football stadium and a commercial centre. The bars are mostly used by the locals, so you will find their prices compare very well with those found in the resort establishments.

TEFÍA

On the same road, heading towards Antigua, the village of Tefía houses the **Ecomuseo de la Alcogida**, a reconstruction of seven typical old Fuerteventuran houses. You can see how a well-to-do family would have lived. There is also an example of a more modest family house, and there are two showing the way of life of artisans. Traditional handicrafts are demonstrated (and sold), and there are exhibitions, a film show and a bar. The everyday necessities of village life had to be made locally, so there are workshops illustrating how carpenters, metalworkers, potters and stonemasons supplied all that was needed for domestic use. You can

also see breadmaking (and sample the results), openwork embroidery and weaving. There is a restaurant, too. ☎ 928 175 434 ⏰ 10.00–18.00 Tues–Sat, closed Sun & Mon

LOS MOLINOS

Los Molinos is west of Tefía, signposted 'Las Parcelas'. This hamlet is one of the few remaining out-of-the-way refuges for local people. There is no electricity, and no clean running water. Mobile phones are also out of range. Five or six caravans are permanently parked here, beside a huddle of a dozen or so small fishermen's houses which are only occupied during the summer months. There is space for two or three cars, and room for a few more on the other side of a stream for those brave enough to attempt the ford.

The black sand and pebble beach is bordered on either side by rocks from which the fishermen cast their lines. In summer, this beach is golden. Fish is the order of the day in the restaurant shack – you can choose from whatever fish has just been caught. A terrace supplies much-needed shade from the sun.

CASILLAS DEL ÁNGEL

About 12 km (7½ miles) west of Puerto del Rosario on the Betancuria road is a small, attractive and spread-out village of old houses. In the village, seek refreshment at **Bar La Cantina**, which is small and unostentatious. The large and (from the outside) rather nice-looking restaurant next door tends to serve as a stopping place for coaches. It is busy, with long trestle tables and little personality. ⓐ Las Casillas del Ángel 39 ☎ 928 538 204

◆ *La Casa de los Coronoles, La Oliva*

Central Fuerteventura

ANTIGUA

For just one year (between 1835 and 1836), Antigua was the island's capital. However, it was not economically viable, and La Oliva, further north, became the capital until 1860, when the honour was given to Puerto del Rosario. This little town, now the administrative centre for several surrounding villages, is a mixture of old and modern buildings, the most noticeable being the new town hall and police station. Opposite these two is the church of **Nuestra Señora de Antigua** (Our Lady of Antigua), which was built in 1785 and has a beautifully carved teak roof – especially over the altar which is colourful and gently gilded. The church is on one side of an attractive square which has a number of old trees.

In May or June every year folklore groups and craftspeople from all over the islands meet to demonstrate publicly their skills and sell their products at the **Feria Insular de Artesanía**, which is held on the outskirts of the town (❶ 928 878 004).

On the road to La Ampuyenta there is a well-restored windmill, **Molino de Antigua**, that was used to grind a type of barley. In addition, the mill site features gardens, exhibition rooms, a restaurant and – of course – a craft shop. The road leading you to this centre has the most unusual street lights. They are a very enlarged version of the lanterns that were used before electrification. 🕐 09.30–17.30 Tues–Fri, 09.30–14.00 Sun; closed Mon & Sat

BETANCURIA

Betancuria is tucked away in the hills. It is atmospheric and tranquil, with stunning views as you approach it over the mountains. This enchanting little village, just over 11 km (7 miles) from Antigua and the oldest in the Canary Islands, was the island's capital for many years when it was first colonised. Considering that Fuerteventura is a desert island, you pass a surprising amount of vegetation, including dragos, the unusual trees that are indigenous to the Canaries, and in the past were believed to have magical qualities. There is a *mirador* (viewpoint) from which you have an impressive view, and where you can be entertained by the squabbles of the almost-tame, playful chipmunks.

Betancuria itself, nestling among the mountains, has a decidedly peaceful air about it. The site was chosen by Jean de Bethencourt as a safe place, difficult for the pirates to find. However, this proved not to be the case, for in 1593 pirates pillaged the town, destroying everything and capturing many of the inhabitants for slavery. Its church was not rebuilt until the 17th century. On the drive down to the village, still on the outskirts, there is an attractive roofless building on the left, the ruin of an old Franciscan monastery that was abandoned on the orders of Queen Isabella II of Spain in 1837. It fell into disrepair, although this is not the reason for the absence of the roof, which was dismantled and sold for grain and water during an exceptionally bad drought in the last century. No one, however, seems to remember the exact details! Until it was abandoned, the monks developed their evangelical work and promoted education, the monastery acting as a place of learning.

The **Iglesia de Santa Maria** (Church of St Mary) was first consecrated in the year 1410. In 1426 it was elevated to become a cathedral and bishopric, although no bishop ever came to take up the post. It contains a number of interesting items, all of which are explained during the half-hourly guided tours.

There is a small, interesting museum in Betancuria (🕒 10.00–17.00 Tues–Sat & 11.00–14.00 Sun; closed Mon).

Well worth a stop is Casa Santa Maria, a lovingly restored old house with beams, and in addition a charming patio where you can buy drinks, ice cream and snacks. The restaurant has won Spanish awards for its gastronomy (🅐 Plaza Santa Maria 📞 928 878 282 🕒 11.30–17.30 & 20.00–22.30).

VALLE DE SANTA INÉS

The 17th-century church in Valle de Santa Inés, near to Betancuria, contains a baroque altar and five impressive and beautiful paintings. In the centre of the village there is a mini complex of a restaurant, bar,

○ *Iglesia de Santa María, Betancuria*

supermarket and souvenir shop. The bar is used by the villagers and offers tapas and fine local cheese.

On the outskirts of the village is the **Taller de Artisania Ceramica**, a handmade pottery workshop. Ceramics produced here are by various members of one family, headed by Doña Josefa, in a style unique to Fuerteventura. The methods and colouring have been handed down through the generations. Doña Josefa's sister works close by, patiently producing traditional straw hats. There are few people these days who are prepared to cut and dry the young palm leaves, split them into required widths, plait them, and then laboriously sew each section into a hat shape.

AGUAS VERDES

Aguas Verdes, on the west coast, is a good place to fish from the rocks, if you don't mind a twisting, turning rough-road drive to get here. Take the road to Betancuria and fork right at Llanos de la Concepción. The road follows the river bed, which only flows during the winter months but retains sufficient moisture to sustain the tamarisk trees. You drive through rolling, ochre hills, past a hotel on your left, then continue on down past a few newly built houses to a pebble beach. Apart from the odd tent it is fairly quiet here.

LA AMPUYENTA

La Ampuyenta is a village in the centre of Fuerteventura, close to both Antigua and Betancuria. **Casa Mena La Ampuyenta** is a well-kept, typical village house dating from the 19th century. It was owned by a successful local doctor, born in 1802, who studied and practised in various other islands and countries and specialised in tropical diseases, a topic upon which he frequently lectured. Mena was a true philanthropist who left money to the village to build a hospital, not far away from his house. However, although the hospital was built, there was never enough money actually to run it, and so it stands empty and unused.

It seems a pity that his house does not have any of the doctor's implements to give us an insight into the 'tools of the trade' of that era. 🕐 10.00–18.00 Tues–Sun; closed Mon

PÁJARA

This town is about 10 km (6 miles) south of Betancuria. It is the administrative centre of the largest of the island's six municipalities, reaching way down to Morro del Jable and the southern tip of the island.

The town itself has an enticing shady square surrounded by Indian laurel trees and flowering shrubs, and there is a constant chattering of birds.

The square features a *noria* (waterwheel) that indicates how, with the help of donkeys, camels – or, when necessary, man – water was drawn in days gone by. The church, **Nuestra Señora de la Regla**, built in 1687, has a most unusual door surround, believed to be influenced by Aztec designs. Inside it is wide with sturdy columns down the centre. It has an unusual double altarpiece, both of which are colourful, the left one having floral recesses and doors. There is a beautifully decorated pulpit.

Not far from the square you will find a **Craft Centre** where you can see demonstrations of traditional openwork embroidery and weaving. Many local products are for sale here. 🕐 10.00–13.00 Mon, Tues, Thur & Fri, 11.00–12.00 & 15.00–18.00 Wed; closed Sat, Sun & fiestas

For some home-made local food, try Casa Isaitas (📞 928 161 402 🕐 10.00–18.00 Fri–Wed, also open 20.00–22.00 Fri & Sat, closed Thur).

AJUY

If a gentle day out is what you want, then take the Ajuy road northwest from Pájara. Ajuy is about 11 km (6 miles) along a sleepy valley of agricultural land, following the path of a wide river bed. En route you'll see many tomato sheds (tomatoes are an important part of the island economy) that seem to blend into the countryside, since they are made of sacking the same colour as the earth. There are numerous 'wigwams' erected in the fields or near houses – these are canes put up to dry, ready to be used for staking the tomato plants.

Ajuy itself lies on a black sandy beach and is a mixture of old dwellings and new buildings. It is a small resort, away from the bustle and noise of the island's other resorts. There is a choice of three or four restaurants, all of which serve fish caught on the day. Be bold and try some, even if they are unrecognisable; you can't get fresher than this.

The sea can be rough, so take care bathing. On the plus side, here and all along the west coast, you experience the wildness and power of nature. The rocky seabed and underwater caves are a scuba diver's paradise. On the north side of Ajuy is a well-kept path that snakes around the

◔ *Aztec-influenced door at Nuestra Señora de la Regla church in Pájara*

cliff-side and leads to most unusual sponge-like rock formations, and on to a bay containing a dozen or so little fishing boats. One expects houses around the next corner, but in fact you find a semicircle of caves, giving you a chance to explore one of the oldest inhabited parts of the island.

VEGA DE RÍO PALMAS

Vega, south of Betancuria, is a small and quite insignificant village at first sight, but there is a lot more to it than first meets the eye. The **church** (🕑 11.00–13.00 Tues–Fri, closed Mon; Mass on Sat 18.00) was built in 1660 and houses a statue of **La Virgen de la Peña**, believed to have been brought by Jean de Bethencourt and placed in the church of Betancuria. When Betancuria was ransacked the local people managed

to hide the sculpture, which they did so well that it wasn't rediscovered until the 17th century – in Vega! The Virgin is the patron saint of the Canary Isles, and on the third Saturday in September, people come every year to Vega de Río Palmas from all over the island, in a pilgrimage (see page 106) to celebrate with a magnificent procession followed by a fiesta. A little way past the church a road to the right takes you alongside the river bed and through the rest of the village. Verdant, unspoilt and dotted with old houses, there are probably more animals here than people. Little terraced fields abound, with lush oases consisting of palm trees, bamboo cane and shrubs.

Follow this same road to Las Peñitas, where among the huge boulders you will see metal watermills working to pump up the water from underground. There is both fresh and saline water: the latter is only good for watering tomatoes, while the former is used for both irrigation and drinking. There are at least two *norias* (waterwheels), turned at one time by donkeys or camels, and even sometimes by people. Now they are either in disuse or functioning with the help of a motor. At the end of this there is a reservoir surrounded by reeds and tamarisks, a haven for frogs and birds. All these things are expected in Europe, but remember – this is a desert island!

Do stop for a meal at Don Antonio, or at least a coffee or a glass of wine on the patio of this now beautifully renovated former ruin. Although well kept, the outer appearance of this restaurant does not prepare you for the delights inside. ⓐ Dirección Pza de la Peña, Vega de Río Palmas ⓣ 928 878 857 ⓛ 11.00–17.00 Wed, Thur & Sun, 11.00–22.00 Fri & Sat; closed Mon & Tues; also closed in June and the second week in December

POZO NEGRO

Pozo Negro on the east coast is an expanding fishing village of colourful houses – the sea comes right up to the waterside houses at high tide. The sea itself can be very rough here, so be careful if you enter the water.

Just off the main road down to the village, you will see buildings used for the Feaga (see page 66), with a tree nursery and experimental fields for the growing of tomatoes, potatoes and onions.

Not far from the village, a short stretch of tarmacked road (that quickly becomes a track) takes you down to the remains of a prehistoric village. This settlement consisted of 100 or so crudely built primitive houses. Most of them are in poor condition, but one of them has been reconstructed to give us an idea of what they were originally like. The sheer size of the settlement is astounding and impressive. There are more, similar house remains scattered between here and the coast, often near the site of springs for fresh water.

For a reviving meal of fresh fish or paella try Los Pescadores, right on the waterfront (❶ 928 174 653 ❷ 12.00–21.30).

⏷ *One of Fuerteventura's traditional windmills*

LA FEAGA

In May **Pozo Negro** is home of **La Feaga**, a kind of 'county show' Fuerteventura-style. If you want an island excursion with a difference, this is the place to go. There's everything from the Goat Supreme Championships, Lucha (Canarian wrestling), horse racing, cheese-making and arts and crafts for sale. The show lasts for four days, and be prepared to eat your fill of local food samples. There is also a tree nursery at the site of La Feaga, and a nursery which grows experimental crops of tomatoes, potatoes and onions.

TISCAMANITA

Tiscamanita, on the road south of Antigua on the way to Tuineje, is well worth a visit. In the village square, which is surrounded by bars, there stands a black marble monument to **Manuel Velázquez Cabrera**, the father of the island's government. Nearby, and close to St Mark's church, there stands a medieval crenellated tithe barn in which villagers at one time stored their ten per cent contribution towards the church's upkeep.

The region is steeped in the traditions of agriculture, producing fields of aloe vera, ecologically grown and processed for the modern market. At nightfall, Egyptian vultures, protected birds, roost on the electricity pylons beside the roads. Perfect examples of extinct volcanoes are everywhere, all with names. There is a series of volcanic tubes where some of the ancient inhabitants dwelt.

Just outside the village there is a fascinating **Windmill Centre**, with a peaceful and pretty courtyard. The history of milling in Fuerteventura is presented, and explained by the helpful, knowledgeable and multilingual curator. Milling maize was a social occasion and an opportunity to meet up with other families. ❶ 928 851 400 🕔 09.30–17.30 Tues–Fri & Sun; closed Mon & Sat

Just behind the Windmill Centre there is a very large and slightly run-down, ochre-coloured house. Its owner tried to bring industrialisation

○ *Tuineje's church (see page 68)*

to the grinding of corn. The machinery was brought in, but the scheme never got off the ground, and it remains untouched and unused inside the house.

TUINEJE

An agricultural town, south of Tiscamanita, Tuineje is the administrative centre for eight villages. It sits in a Nature Park which also contains the volcanic peaks La Caldera de Gairia and Los Cuchillos de Vigan. The wide valleys between these two support rather poor vegetation, but the Park is a safe place for several endangered species of birds.

Tuineje's **church** is quite splendid. Completed in 1790, it is dedicated to San Miguel Arcangel. Every 13 October the town celebrates its victory in 1740 against the English pirates who attacked Fuerteventura.

Southern Fuerteventura

LAS PLAYITAS

Las Playitas, southeast of Tuineje and 6 km (3½ miles) north of Gran Tarajal, reminds the visitor of what Fuerteventura used to be like. A few fishermen's cottages border the black sandy beach, on which their sun-bleached and sea-faded boats are pulled up. There is a small harbour with a slipway. Among the winding alleyways there are a few restaurants mostly serving very fresh fish. Should you decide to stay the night, there is accommodation in the village, and if you ask in one of the bars or restaurants they are only too willing to help.

Just outside the village, a narrow winding tarmac road leads to the most unusual and amazing lighthouse, **El Faro de Entillada**, high up on the mountain. It was built in 1953 as a fort with an inner courtyard. The masonry is of black stones with white mortar and red edges. You can walk around outside and will be mesmerised by the crashing waves on the rocks far below. This is not a trip for the faint-hearted or sufferers of vertigo!

GRAN TARAJAL

Just south of Las Playitas, Gran Tarajal is the second-largest town on the island, with a blue-flag beach of black sand. Gran Tarajal has a long and quite handsome promenade where you can sit with a beer, a coffee or an ice cream and watch the world go by.

For some years now more trade has passed through this port than Puerto del Rosario, the capital, and during winter months it is still very busy with the transportation and export of tomatoes. A lot of building and modernising is going on here at the moment, but one fragment of history that remains is the thick-trunked palm grove growing in the town centre, which was planted generations ago to protect crops from the cruel winds. Today this is where the town's health centre is located.

Although today we may no longer understand the importance of lime, it was not too long ago that lime was invaluable, especially as a

● The untouched village of Las Playitas (see page 69)

building material. A huge kiln was built in 1953 on a 6,000 sq m (7,176 sq yd) piece of rustic land near to Gran Tarajal, with a workshop and accommodation for the workforce. Processed lime was mixed with water and used both for whitewashing and constructing houses.

The last fortnight of August, Gran Tarajal hosts a Youth Festival, while in September, since 1995, there has been an annual International Fishing Competition for big-game fish such as blue and white marlin. Once caught and weighed, the fish are tagged and returned to the sea.

Gran Tarajal Auditorium An important island venue for concerts and dances. ☎ 928 162 449 ✉ jal@yahoo.es 🕐 10.00–13.00, 17.00–21.00 Mon–Sat; closed Sun

TAKING A BREAK

Confradías de Pescadores ££ Local restaurant serving fresh fish. 📍 Recinto Portuario s/n ☎ 928 162 074 🕐 08.00–23.00 Mon–Sat, 08.00–17.00 Sun

Da Nonna Diana ££ Traditional Italian cuisine is on the menu here. 📍 Avenida Paco Hierro 6 ☎ 928 162 339 🕐 21.00–02.00; closed Wed

Restaurante Avenida Italia ££ Specialising in Italian cuisine. 📍 Avenida Paco Hierro 9 ☎ 928 162 209 🕐 12.00–24.00 Wed–Mon; closed Tues

Restaurante Balandro ££ Fresh fish and meat. 📍 Avenida Paco Hierro 8 ☎ 928 162 359 🕐 12.00–16.00, 17.00–24.00; closed Tues Nov–Apr

Restaurante Chino Oso Panda ££ Chinese cooking. 📍 Calle Atis Tirma 11 ☎ 928 162 526 🕐 12.00–16.30, 19.00–24.00

Restaurante – Tapas la Marisma de Gran Tarajal ££ 📍 Avenida Paco Hierro 19 ☎ 928 165 113 🕐 09.30–24.00 (summer); closed Mon in winter

GINIGINAMAR

This delightful little fishing village with a black sandy beach is 4 km
(2½ miles) off the main coastal road and southwest of Gran Tarajal.
Giniginamar is totally unspoilt, and a reminder of what many of
the tourist resorts used to be like before they were commercialised.
This protected 'area of biological interest' is a good place to dive.
There are a couple of discreetly modernised apartments for holiday lets,
and a nicely situated bar-cum-restaurant called **Olas del Sur** with a few
tables outside, overlooking the sea (ⓐ C del Carmen 5 ❶ 669 892 549).

TARAJALEJO

Further down the coast, this little fishing village, on the east coast of
the Jandía Peninsula, is to be found at the end of a palm-covered valley.
It has a fine, black-sand beach and a small harbour. Apart from the small
aquarium (**El Centro de Ocio El Brasero** ⓐ Carretera General Tarajalejo
❶ 928 161 351 ❶ 10.00–20.00 Tues–Sun; closed Mon), the village is really
only notable for the sports facilities that have become established here,
making it a day-out venue of choice for many holidaymakers.

Quad biking Excursions include the bikes, transfer from your hotel,
security gear, training, snacks and beverages. ❶ 928 161 372
❶ 09.00–17.00 Mon–Fri, weekends by arrangement
Quad Safari To arrange this excursion, you must reserve a place.
There are pick-up points in Jandía and Costa Calma.

After an introduction in Tarajalejo, you set off for the west coast and
the SS *American Star*, where there is a break for sandwiches and drinks
(included in the price). The tour covers approximately 80 km (50 miles),
half on tarmacked roads and half on dirt tracks. Return mid-afternoon
for transport back to your pick-up point. Driving licence, passport and
sensible footwear are necessities; a T-shirt and extra water in a backpack
are recommended. ❶ 928 161 372 (same company as quad biking)
❶ 09.00 (Jandía) and 09.30 (Costa Calma)
Motor trekking Run by an ex-professional biker, **Fuertenduro** does
off-road excursions. Driving licence, passport and sensible footwear

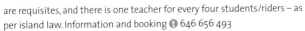

are requisites, and there is one teacher for every four students/riders – as per island law. Information and booking ☏ 646 656 493
🌐 www.fuertenduro.com

Karting There is a kart track in the village of Cardón, just north of Tarajalejo. ☏ 620 504 399 🕐 10.00–20.00

Horse riding The **Centro Hipico**, based at El Centro de Ocio (see opposite), offers horse riding and trekking. ☏ 928 161 351

LA LAJITA

La Lajita is a coastal village inhabited mainly by local people, a few minutes' drive off the main coastal road southwest of Giniginamar and Tarajalejo. Very unspoilt, the village merits a visit just to have a swim, a coffee or even a meal. However, the main attraction for most visitors is the zoo, **La Lajita Oasis Park**. Set amidst lush tropical gardens, including a cactus garden, the park is home to a wide variety of birds, reptiles, primates and other mammals. Twice daily there are parrot shows, and you can try riding a camel. There are also reptile shows and a 'birds of prey' show. There is a bar and restaurant, with rustic wooden tables and benches beneath palm-leaf sunshades. ⓐ Carretera General de Jandía s/n ☏ 928 161 135 ☏ 928 343 047 🌐 www. lajitaoasispark.com 🕐 9.00–18.00 ❶ Admission charge

LA PARED

This small village on the southwest coast of Fuerteventura is notable for its multicoloured beaches. To the south, **La Playa del Viejo Rey**, is golden sand; immediately north is **La Playa de la Pared**, made of pebbly, black volcanic sand. La Pared (which means The Wall) is said to have marked the boundary in days gone by between two rival kingdoms, the Maxorata and Jandía. Now, however, nothing remains of the wall except the myth. The coast is one of sheltered bays and extensive dunes. The sea can be a little rough, though. Major roads in the area are paved, but access to the beaches is often by way of dirt tracks.

 *La Lajita (see page 73)*

Cowabunga Surf School Courses for all ages from eight years upwards. Equipment is included for all courses, together with free shuttle service from all hotels in the Costa Calma area, including Jandía. ☎ 928 549 122 ✉ info@cowabunga.de 🕐 10.00–18.00

Riding stables ☎ 928 174 151/619 275 389 🕐 10.00–12.00 & 16.00–18.00

TAKING A BREAK

Restaurant/Bar Bahia Mar This child-friendly restaurant has a panoramic view of the coast and is wonderful for a family day out. The fish on the menu is straight from the sea below. 🕐 12.00–16.00, 18.00–22.00

COFETE
To reach Cofete, take the winding road from Morro del Jable across the Jandía Peninsula and travel on about 20 km (12 miles) of track that only allows for single-file traffic in some places. It is best to do this in a four-wheel-drive. The village is in an isolated part of Fuerteventura in the mountain mass of Jandía, the peak of which, Pico de la Zarza, is the highest point of the island at 807 m (2,648 ft).

The area is a Natural Park, and you will find that it has the most wonderful views of the island, while on a really clear day you can see other islands to the west. This is a superb area in which to go walking or trekking, but remember to make sure that you take plenty of water with you – and protection from the sun. Also, let someone know your plans. You will find yourself at one with nature, with only the sound of birdsong, the wind and the waves – it's definitely a place to get away from it all, clear the mind and calm the body. Down on the coast, you can walk and walk on the extensive pristine sands. There is a tiny fishing village, with a restaurant well known for its fish stew. The beaches are often deserted and spectacularly beautiful, with wild seas, and often, very dangerous breakers, crashing onto the shore. As the sea recedes you will find small birds darting about looking for food brought in by the water.

Hidden in these wild surroundings is the house of **Gustav Winter**, which has many varying myths surrounding it. Winter was a German scientist who did not agree with the Nazi regime. He escaped from Germany to Fuerteventura, where he laboriously built his unique hideaway, bringing in all the building materials by donkey and camel. There are rumours of secret tunnels leading to his house, but these have never been substantiated. Some say he was a true benefactor, giving money to local nuns to ensure the children had one good meal a day; and he was responsible for bringing the first electricity to the island. Other rumours paint a darker image of a man who used this fortress-like villa as a refuge for top Nazis. Whatever the truth, the fact remains that a visit to this secluded villa is worth the difficult journey.

⬥ *The amazing landscape of the Jandía Peninsula*

The Jandía Peninsula

This area, which includes the resorts of Costa Calma and Morro del Jable, is a nature reserve of great beauty and variety. The Parque Natural de Jandía covers 2,688 hectares (6,642 acres) and ranges from the incredibly white sand, turquoise-sea-fringed beaches of the east coast, to the wilder seas around the west coast's rocky shores. Between the two coasts are hilly ranges, plateaus and plains. This is a very varied and special environment, home to much of the island's wildlife, including a number of species of birds of prey and night birds, such as owls. A salt-marsh area entices birds such as dunlin, and there are several specialised plant communities. The highest peak is Pico de la Zarza at 807 m (2,648 ft), which is often covered by clouds creating a microclimate.

If walking is on your agenda, the hills and valleys of Jandía offer an enormous range of scenery, with spectacular vistas of both sea and land. Silence prevails here, broken only by the cry of the birds or the whistling of the wind.

The beaches on the east coast seem to go on for ever and can be over 1 km (½ mile) wide in some places. Here you can guarantee you will be able to find your own special piece of paradise among the little coves. Words cannot properly describe the total wonderment of this area; you have to go and see for yourself. Do remember, if you are on these isolated beaches, to take plenty of water to drink, and don't forget protection from the sun. You will not find bars or restaurants in the wilder areas, just sand, sea and surf.

PARK REGULATIONS

Remember that it is prohibited in the Jandía Natural Park to:

- Light fires
- Leave rubbish
- Collect any of the plant species
- Camp or use vehicles outside the authorised areas

Lanzarote & Lobos

A day trip to Lanzarote, Fuerteventura's neighbour to the north, is a major attraction. The smaller island is just 40 minutes away on a pleasant sea crossing. The following organised excursions have pick-up points at Corralejo and El Cotillo. Ask in your hotel or apartments, or see your tour rep, for times and the nearest pick-up point. Many inclusive trips also take in a visit to tiny, unspoilt Lobos Island, which is just 3 km (2 miles) offshore from Corralejo.

SUGGESTED TOURS

Lanzarote South Tour

Scheduled for an early start on Mondays, Thursdays and Saturdays. After a 40-minute ferry trip to Lanzarote you arrive in **Playa Blanca**, the most rapidly and well-planned developing tourist area. You head for coffee at **Yaiza**, one of Lanzarote's most attractive villages. Then it's on to an optional camel ride over a volcanic landscape, followed by a fascinating tour of **Timanfaya**, a protected National Park consisting of fields of lava, the result of an eruption lasting from 1730 to 1736. Evidence of the continuing ground heat will be dramatically demonstrated.

The next stop is for lunch amidst the island's wine growing area, with an opportunity to sample some of the local wine. The last visit of the tour will be to **El Golfo**, a rugged coastal area, a unique green lagoon and the salt fields of El Janubio.

Returning to Fuerteventura, you will arrive back at your starting point at about 17.00.

Lanzarote Grand Tour

This tour takes place on Tuesdays, Thursdays and Saturdays. After the ferry crossing to Lanzarote, the Grand Tour starts with coffee in Yaiza, and continues to the National Park of Timanfaya. This is followed by lunch, and a wine-tasting in the surrounding vineyards. The route then heads towards the north, passing the **Monument al Campesino**

⬥ *The stunning volcanic landscape of Lanzarote*

(Monument to the Countryman) in the centre of the island created by César Manrique. Next comes **Teguise**, the island's old capital, and up to the spectacular Famara cliffs, called **El Risco de Famara**. Here there is a short stop at the viewpoint overlooking much of the northern part of the Island.

The tour continues through **Haría**, the valley of a thousand palm trees, and on to the famous caves, made so beautiful by César Manrique (see below). You are then taken back along the east of the island to Playa Blanca for the return ferry trip across to Fuerteventura.

César Manrique Tour

The César Manrique Tour takes place on Fridays. Going straight from the ferry in Playa Blanca to the centre of the Island, where stands the Manrique monument dedicated to the farmers of Lanzarote, the tour will continue through the old capital of Teguise and stop for coffee at a viewpoint. Next on the itinerary is another viewpoint, **Mirador del Rio**, cleverly designed by the artist to blend into the cliffside. It offers spectacular views to the north. From here the coach descends to a choice of either the **Cueva de los Verdes** (Green Caves), which are natural and lead to an unexpected optical illusion, or **Jameos del Agua Caves** where you will be filled with wonder at how one man could envisage transforming an underground volcanic tube into an Aladdin's cave. There is a restaurant, a little natural seawater lake, dance floor, bars and an exotic palm-fringed swimming pool (now purely decorative). All this is landscaped, with curving steps, plants and water, complementing the colours and textures of the rocks.

On to **Punta de Mujeres**, a sprawling fishing village and favourite summer resort for islanders, where there is a lunchtime stop.

The **Cactus Gardens** are the next port of call. These were the last creation of César Manrique before he died in a car accident in 1992. The highlight of this trip is a visit to the **Fundación César Manrique**, the artist's former home, which he designed in and above part of the lava flow. It is an incredible example of the skill of this man, who knew how to connect nature, life and art so successfully.

Lanzarote shopping

Although the seven Canary Islands are not very far apart, they all have something different to offer. Lanzarote is quite different to Fuerteventura in both its natural landscape and its facilities for shopping.

Leaving Corralejo at 09.00 on Tuesdays, Thursdays and Saturdays, the ferry will arrive in Playa Blanca approximately 40 minutes later. A coach takes you to **Arrecife**, the modern capital of the Island, to spend two hours shopping and sampling street cafés. The coach then takes you to a small but modern shopping centre, **The Biosphere** in Puerto del Carmen, the hub of tourism on Lanzarote. Catch the ferry at 16.00, to arrive back at your hotel at about 17.00.

Timanfaya National Park

One learns about volcanoes in school, and of course they are seen from time to time on television, but, as with so many things, to experience their results at first hand is altogether another story. The sheer scale of the eruption, the solidified lava flow creating unusual rock forms, the colours, the sulphuric smells, and even today the heat so near the surface, all leave an incredible impression.

ISLA DE LOS LOBOS (ISLAND OF SEALS)

This lovely island is small, just 470 hectares (1,161 acres), and the highest point is **Montaña de la Caldera**, 127 m (417 ft) above sea level. It is home to over 130 species of plant and a variety of birdlife – but no seals. A circular walk around this beautiful and unspoilt island takes between three and four hours.

The whole area is a protected nature zone, so visitors need to obey certain rules: for example, keep to the marked paths; do not light a fire outside the designated areas; do not leave or bury rubbish; do not remove any plants. To camp on the island you need to obtain authorisation from the Central Government (El Cabildo) of Fuerteventura, as you do if you want to gain access to the top of La Caldera.

▶ *Windmills are a landmark in the countryside*

Food & drink

Canarios, like other Spaniards, love to eat out with friends and family, tucking into their food with a robust appetite, sharing noisy, convivial conversation, and letting children run and play around the table (there is no Spanish word for 'bedtime', and parents rarely go out without their children). Only the very smartest places demand any degree of formality. Apart from a light early breakfast of coffee and a pastry, meal times tend to be late by north European standards; about 14.00 for lunch and 21.00 for dinner. However, an exception is made for tourists. In the resorts, meals are served at all times of day. It is not unusual to see locals finishing lunch while tourists are beginning their evening meal. The standard of food on Fuerteventura is generally good, and it is reasonably priced.

INTERNATIONAL EATING

It would be perfectly possible to spend a fortnight on the island and have nothing but Italian food, for example – and many holidaymakers do just that. With the local population so outnumbered by tourists, restaurants increasingly offer an international dining experience, with a variety of familiar home-from-home dishes like soups, steak and chips or omelettes. Paella and sangria are not local to Fuerteventura, coming from the Iberian peninsula, though both are to be found in the larger resorts. Needless to say, you will also find there the ubiquitous fish fingers and chips for the children, along with pasta and pizza, and Chinese and Indian cuisine.

GOFIO

For centuries *gofio* has been the staple food of the Canary Islands. It is relatively easy to make from toasted grains of maize, wheat or barley, ground into flour. The flour is kneaded with either milk or water, sometimes with a little crumbled goat's cheese or honey added. The dough is then twisted into sticks and used as a type of bread.

It was easy for the island's goatherds or fishermen, who were often away for days at a time, to take these sticks of *gofio* with them as staple

⬥ Majorero *cheese coated with paprika is a speciality*

provisions; it rarely went off and was very sustaining. Breakfast today, for locals, often still consists of milky coffee with *gofio*.

Local soups and stews – for example *potaje*, *puchero* and *sancocho* – are thickened with *gofio* flour, making them more substantial.

MOJO

The most uniquely Canarian phrase on the menu is *con mojo*, 'with *mojo*'. Grilled or fried fish, roasted meats, or boiled vegetables, almost anything may be served *con mojo*. *Mojo* (pronounced 'mo-ho') is the piquant sauce of the Canary Islands. Based on olive oil, it comes in different versions, and in good restaurants is more or less spicy according to what it accompanies. *Mojo* comes in two colours – red and green. Coriander and parsley make *mojo verde* (green *mojo*), which has a refreshing bite, while hot chillis are used in the spicier *mojo rojo* (red *mojo*).

TAPAS

This is good way to try out a variety of local dishes. Tapas are small portions of food (*tapa* means lid or small dish), often served as a side dish. The problem can be in knowing what to ask for. Normally there is a good selection of tapas on display in either chilled or heated cabinets on the bar. If you want a portion, ask for *una ración* (pronounced *rass-ee-on*).

GOAT'S CHEESE

Mojo is the perfect accompaniment for fried or grilled goat's cheese (*queso de cabra*), served as a delicious starter. Cheese has an important part in the local diet, and is often eaten as tapas or with a glass of wine. Local to Fuerteventura, *majorero* is a traditional Fuerteventuran speciality and a gourmet's delight, acclaimed throughout Spain. It is a mix of goat's and sheep's milk with a dense texture and strong but smooth flavour. Older *majorero* can be coated with oil and paprika or *gofio*. The local goat's cheese is delicious and is categorised as follows:

Fresco – a fresh, soft and moist white cheese.

Semi-curado – left to mature for a month and is of a firmer texture.

Curado – after two months it begins to dry, becoming a harder cheese.

Viejo – at least six months old, by which time it is almost as hard as Parmesan, which it resembles.

MEAT

Wild game and pork are the favourites of the islanders. Goats are ubiquitous on Fuerteventura – everywhere you go you'll see goats, either in herds or tethered singly. They are hardy, easy to look after, and have been one of the island's main sources of meat. Very tasty, goat is usually served roasted (*al horno*) or in a stew. Rabbits were introduced by the first settlers and they bred well. They became a staple source of fresh meat for the islanders. Fuerteventura's rabbit population was not subjected to the ravages of myxomatosis, and they are very plentiful. Rabbit dishes continue to be popular today. Pigs are kept on the island, to a much lesser extent than goats, and island-bred pork is full of flavour.

Puchero is a classic Canarian stew, thick and savoury, made with lentils, chickpeas, vegetables and two or more kinds of meat, including pork.

◆ *Goats are very common in Fuerteventura and provide essential meat*

CHURROS

A firm batter is formed into long-sausage-like shapes and then deep-fried, not unlike traditional fairground doughnuts. Traditionally *churros* were dipped in a thick chocolate drink (*churros con chocolate*); nowadays they can be either sweet or savoury and are also dipped in coffee.

FISH

Since most of the coastal resorts were formerly fishing ports, it is not surprising that fish is an island staple. More unexpected is that on Fuerteventura traditionally fish is salted and preserved instead of being eaten fresh. Because of seasonal food shortages in the past, various kinds of plentiful fish were preserved when caught – gutted as soon as possible and hung up in the sun until dry. This practice continues today. Another way of preservation is to salt the fish, which is then used to make a dish called *Sancocho*, still a traditional island favourite. *Sancocho* is a fish stew made with potatoes and vegetables.

FRUIT & VEGETABLES

These are very fresh, in spite of the fact that the majority come from either other Canarian islands or mainland Spain. Potatoes are a staple – a typical local dish is *papas Arrugadas* (locally grown, very wrinkly potatoes cooked in their skins with a salty crust). These are especially good eaten with either *mojo verde* or *mojo rojo*.

DESSERTS

Canarios have a sweet tooth, and may finish a meal with the islanders' traditional dessert, *bienmesabe*, a syrupy, nutty concoction, often served with ice cream. *Gofio* desserts are rather stodgy and syrupy, but *flan gofio* or *frangollo*, flavoured with lemon, is quite delicious.

WINE

Unlike its neighbour, Lanzarote, Fuerteventura produces very little wine, and that which is made, mainly around La Oliva, Tetir and Casillas del Ángel, is for home consumption.

Menu decoder

SNACKS/SIDE ORDERS/TAPAS

Aceitunas en mojo Olives in hot sauce

Bocadillo (pronounced *bocadee-yo*) Filled roll

Chipirones Small squid

Ensalada Salad

Gambas ajillo Garlic prawns

Perrito caliente Hot-dog

Queso Cheese

Tapas Snacks

STARTERS

Potage Thick vegetable soup – may contain added meat

Potage de berros Watercress soup

MAIN COURSES

Cabrito Kid (goat)

Caldo de escado Fish, vegetables and maize meal stew

Conejo al salmorejo Rabbit in hot chilli sauce

Garbanzasa Chickpea stew with meat

Lomo Slices of pork

Pata de cerdo Roast leg of pork

Pechuga empanada Breaded chicken breast or chicken breast in batter

Puchero Meat and vegetable stew

Ranchos Noodles, beef and chickpeas

Ropa vieja Chickpeas, vegetables and potatoes (although meat can be added)

Sancocho Salted fish (often *cherne*, a kind of sea bass) with potatoes and sweet potatoes

DESSERTS

Arroz con leche Cold rice pudding

Bienmesabe A mix of honey and almonds (delicious poured over ice cream)

Flan Crême caramel

Fruta del tiempo Fresh fruit in season

Helado Ice cream

Truchas Turnovers filled with pumpkin jam

DRINKS

Agua (pronounced *ah-whah*)
  mineral Mineral water
  con gas/sin gas Fizzy/still
Batido Milkshake
Café Coffee
  con leche Made with milk
  cortado Small white coffee
  descafeinado
  Decaffeinated
  solo Black
Cerveza Beer
Leche Milk
Limonada Lemonade
Naranja Orange
Ron Local rum
Té Tea
Vino Wine
  blanco White
  rosado Rosé
  tinto Red

SPECIALITY DRINKS

Bitter kas Similar to Campari but non-alcoholic
Cocktail Atlantico Rum, dry gin, banana liqueur, blue curaçao, pineapple nectar
Cocktail Canario Rum, banana cream liqueur, orange juice, cointreau, a drop of grenadine
Guindilla Rum-based cherry liqueur
Mora Blackberry liqueur
Ron miel Rum with honey, a local speciality
Sangria Mix of red wine, spirits and fruit juices; can be made with champagne on request

Shopping

Although part of the EU, the Canary Islands have a special duty-free status. Therefore they are treated as a non-EU region for allowances. You will probably find it is very tempting to spend a lot on duty-free goods – the prices are often lower than in the UK. But be warned – when you return home, there is a limit to the value of goods you are allowed to bring in without attracting tax. These allowances vary, and they do apply to tobacco, alcohol and perfume. Check with your travel agent before you leave.

It is difficult to be specific about shop opening hours. Local shops typically open from 09.00–13.00 and 16.30–19.30 or 20.00 in the week (everything shuts down for *siesta* in the afternoon heat). On Saturdays, local shops usually close for the day at 13.00. In tourist centres they tend to open from 10.00–22.00 (supermarkets 08.30–21.00).

All resorts have shopping centres with good supermarkets. There are some colourful open-air markets in various tourist areas, starting early and finishing at about 13.00.

You can expect to bargain at markets, and at many of the duty-free shops in tourist resorts. When making a large purchase, be sure that you get a proper money-back guarantee, and if appropriate that an international warranty is included and is properly completed. Beware

MARKETS

Most island communities have open-air markets. You will find a huge selection of things to buy and it is fun to haggle. Most take place in the morning.

Caleta de Fuste Saturday – Castillo Plaza
Corralejo Monday and Friday – Baku Complex, on the main road to La Oliva
Costa Calma Sunday
Morro del Jable Thursday – Avenida Saladar

of scams, and be sure to check all receipts before paying, including those from restaurants. Beware also of counterfeit goods, and treat any bargain-priced electrical goods and cameras as suspect. Souvenir shops are everywhere, but their goods, apart from local crafts, are not necessarily made in Fuerteventura.

TRADITIONAL CRAFTS

Openwork embroidery This is one of the oldest traditional crafts in the Canary Islands, dating back to the days of the early settlers. You will see traycloths, table runners and mats, aprons, handkerchiefs and little dolls. It is possible to see women working away at many of the craft centres dotted throughout the island.

◐ *You'll find multicoloured woven bags and baskets on sale in the markets*

Weaving Again, this dates back to the days of the early settlers. You will find handwoven bags, material for costumes worn by the folklore groups, blankets and rugs.

Basketwork This is a really functional part of the local handicrafts, the raw material being palm leaves which are found in abundance. Originally there was a large demand for basketwork for domestic and personal use. Nowadays, basketwork is almost exclusively ornamental.

Green palm leaves are made into saddle bags, mats, brooms and grain storage baskets. Strips of green palm leaf are woven for moulding cheese. White palm leaves are made into hats, sewing baskets and fans.

Pottery The ancient inhabitants of the island, the 'Majos', introduced the making of earthenware pottery from the north of Africa. Aboriginal pottery was shaped by hand and was typically oval with a conical or flat bottom, the surface being decorated with dots or slashes. When the island was colonised this typical design was abandoned and different shapes, sizes and modes of decoration were adopted.

The robust pottery is still made by hand without using a wheel or moulds. The most common artefacts are cooking pots, baking dishes and fertility symbols.

The *zurron* This is a bag made from the skin of a goat kid. It is used to knead *gofio* (see page 84). The *zurron* is one of the most common artefacts found throughout the island history.

Olivina Olivina is a Canarian volcanic, green, semi-precious stone that is made into jewellery, which you will find for sale at reasonable prices.

LIFESTYLE

Children

Fuerteventura is a very child-friendly place where families are made welcome in restaurants, bars or entertainments. The tolerant attitude towards children ensures that they too will have a good holiday. Off the beach there are enough activities to keep them happily occupied.

You will find that nearly all villages have a designated playground area with swings, slides and other amusements. These are usually close to the centre and well constructed. Locals will go out of their way to pander to the young – in a busy Canarian bar, if a child struggles up onto a stool and asks for a glass of water, he or she will be served immediately!

For young children on a bucket-and-spade holiday, Fuerteventura is a paradise. So much sand, so little time to build all those sand castles! Lots of fun can be had among the sand dunes near Corralejo (see page 16), with dunes rising to heights of 10 m (30 ft) or more, but children will need strict supervision, as the sea around Fuerteventura can be rough. Paddling is great, too, with no worrying about treading on rocks. As there is so often a breeze, kite-flying is great fun.

ACTIVITIES FOR CHILDREN

There are many boating and diving activities available at all the resorts, but many only cater for children over 12 years old. Baku, in Corralejo (see page 17), however, has facilities for all children, young and old. Tennis, riding, go-karting and camel rides are within easy reach of most tourist centres (see individual Resorts, pages 13–52), and many of the Excursions (see pages 53–82) are also suitable for families. Other places of special interest for children are the aquarium in Tarajalejo and the zoo park in La Lajita (see below).

La Lajita Oasis Park

Set amidst lush tropical gardens in the Oasis Park in the village of La Lajita (see page 73), this small zoo park is home to a wide variety of birds, reptiles, primates and other mammals. Twice daily there are parrot

⬥ Camels are built for children!

shows, but the highlight for children is the 30-minute camel safari. Treks take place throughout the day according to demand. Ponies and donkeys are also available for rides, and feeding of the crocodiles takes place around once a week. There is a bar and restaurant and also a souvenir shop. ❶ 928 343 047 ❷ 9.00–18.00 ❶ Admission charge

El Centro de Ocio El Brasero

There is an aquarium just outside the village of Tarajalejo (see page 72), which has three large tanks of Canarian fish. ❶ Carretera General Tarajalejo ❶ 928 161 351 ❷ Tues–Sun 10.00–20.00; closed Mon

Carnival

This is a dazzling show that takes place all over the island (see page 104). Much of the spectacle revolves around the crowning of the Carnival Queen. The funfairs (which don't usually get going until around 19.00) are great for the children, and they will also enjoy the noise, colour and flamboyance of the parade.

STAY SAFE IN THE SUN

Be careful of the strength of the sun in Fuerteventura. When it is windy, the temperature can seem deceptively cool. A high-factor sunblock is a must and it is sensible for children to wear a hat, preferably one with elastic under the chin to stop it being blown away!

Sports & activities

Fuerteventura is an ideal place for activities on both land and water.
Walking, riding and cycling are readily available, and the hiking is
superb – there's something for all levels of fitness and there are no real
restrictions on walking wherever you want. The snorkelling is wonderful
and the scuba diving even better.

SUGGESTED WALKING & HIKING ROUTES

None of the routes described below is difficult, and they are designed to
take no more than half a day to accomplish. They will all give you wonderful
views. When walking, be mindful of crops, do not damage walls you may
have to cross, or disturb the domesticated animals. Make sure you wear
proper shoes, and remember to take a hat, suncream and drinking water.
It is a wise precaution to let someone know where you plan to go.

Tuineje–Toto

Set off from Tuineje, go past the cemetery and continue until you reach
the top of Mount Manitaga, where you will enjoy magnificent views
over the whole island. Go down along the road towards Toto. Examples
of the native flora and fauna can be seen along this route.
Estimated time Between 3 and 4 hours
Degree of difficulty Average

Tiscamanita–Pozo Negro

Leave Tiscamanita and go along the ravine, through an aloe vera
plantation, until you reach the Caldera de la Laguna. After you have
crossed the Malpais Grande, you will reach Pozo Negro.
Estimated time Between 3 and 4 hours
Degree of difficulty Average

Lajares–Corralejo

From Lajares take the path to the Calderon Hondo volcanoes. Follow the
Majanicho road, which will take you into the volcanic area known as

⬥ *Kite surfers on Flag Beach near Corralejo*

Mascona. There are wonderful views towards Lajares and the southern part of the island along this stretch of the route. Calderon Hondo is a circular volcanic cone that is around 70 m (230 ft) deep. The Caldera Encantada is well worth visiting, before continuing through the Morro del Fraile to Corralejo.

Estimated time Between 3 and 4 hours
Degree of difficulty Average

El Malpais de la Arena

Located in the north of the island, this route starts close to Villaverde. The stretch from the Montaña del Molino to the Montaña de los Saltos runs beside the walls that separate El Malpais de la Arena from the farming land around Villaverde. From La Hoya del Agua, you will get a beautiful view over the northern part of Fuerteventura. The old lava flows from the Villaverde volcanoes and those that make up El Malpais de la Arena can be seen clearly. From the base of the Montaña de la Arena you can look across and see the Isla de los Lobos and Lanzarote.

Estimated time Between 3 and 4 hours
Degree of difficulty Average

Barranco de la Herradura (Puerto del Rosario)

The route starts from just outside Puerto del Rosario, at the mouth of the ravine that runs to Time. As you progress along this route, you will be able to see the ruins of early settlements, and local flora and fauna.

Estimated time 3 hours
Degree of difficulty Easy

Barranco de los Molinos

Located 4 km (2½ miles) from Tefía, the Barranco is a deep and wide ravine that runs down into the sea, and is home to many of the island's native plants.

Estimated time Between 2 and 3 hours
Degree of difficulty Easy

Barranco de Butihondo–Pico de la Zarza

Located in the southern part of the island, this is a small route along the Barranco de Butihondo which will take you to the top of the highest point of the island, at 807 m (2,648 ft). From the peak, on a clear day you will be able to see some of the islands to the west.

Estimated time Approximately 3 hours
Degree of difficulty Average

Cañada del Rio–La Pared

This walk is in the southwest of the island. It is a fascinating route through the Island's most desert-like region, where you will get magnificent views over the enormous El Jable dunes, the amazing coastline and the wild and turbulent sea.

Estimated time Approximately 3 hours
Degree of difficulty Easy

Barranco de la Vega–Malpaso

Located in the centre of the island, this route follows the path of the barranco, a large ravine, past a tiny dam and down through some surprising mountains, where you can visit a delightful chapel said to be the site of an appearance by Our Lady of La Peña.

Estimated time Approximately 2 hours
Degree of difficulty Easy

Caleta de Fuste–Salinas del Carmen

This walk was part of the road that joined Puerto del Rosario and Antigua. The route starts from the beach at Caleta de Fuste, and is an opportunity to visit Caleta's fortified castle. Walk south along the shore of the beach and past the lime kilns at La Guirra. The destination is the only working salt mine left on the island. There is a tiny fishing village in the area, where you can either stop at the beach or continue south to the ravine known as the Barranco de la Torre.

Estimated time Approximately 3 hours
Degree of difficulty Easy

● *Fuerteventuran waters are great for windsurfing*

WILDLIFE WATCHING

Because Fuerteventura is a desert-like island, wildlife has to struggle harder in order to survive. Two of the island's endangered species are the Egyptian vulture and the Houbara bustard, both of which are protected. The Houbara bustard is at last making good progress and breeding well. However, the Egyptian vulture is still struggling to increase its numbers, partly due to the changing environment in Fuerteventura over the years, and the fact that the young birds do not become sexually active until five or six years old.

Rabbits do well here, vying with the goats for food. The chipmunks or ground squirrels, although not a native species (they were originally brought from North Africa), increase each year. There are the usual rats and mice, and most strangely the island supports a population of hedgehogs.

Under the water the bays and rock pools teem with varied and colourful specimens. Snorkelling is an absolute delight, not only for seeing the fish, but for the profusion of plant life. Scuba diving is even better. Sometimes, if you are really lucky, you might see whales, dolphins and turtles.

WINDSURFING & KITEBOARDING

Just south of Costa Calma on **Playa de Sotavento**, the PWA/ISA Windsurfing World Cup Championship is held every year at the end of July, followed immediately by the World Kiteboarding Grand Prix. These spectacular competitions attract the best boarders in the world, competing for thousands of euros in prize money. The area is known for its strong, gusty offshore winds, which can reach up to 50 knots (almost 100 km/h), so you can be sure to see some breathtaking moments, and will be able to admire the great bravery and skill of the participants. The temptation to emulate the contestants is strong, and the southern part of the island always attracts a large number of surfing fans.

Festivals & events

Festivals, or fiestas, are an integral part of Canarian life. They are partly religious, with recreational and cultural activities taking place at the same time. The whole community joins in, either with the preparations or just by being there, and everyone becomes involved with the infectious exuberance.

Island fiestas are characterised by colourful processions, complete with donkey carts laden with sustenance for the forthcoming hours – and also available for both children and the elderly to hitch a ride when in need of a rest. The celebrations are accompanied by masses of eating and drinking, dancing and folk music.

Age-old games are played, sometimes with competitions between nearby villages. Stalls have a fairground feel about them, offering sweets and amusements for children and alcoholic pick-me-ups for the adults. In the evening there are concerts, plays and dancing, with rock groups hired for the younger generation. In some of the more isolated villages, you can still see black-clad grandmas or maiden aunts sitting on benches around the dance floor, following the old chaperone rules! All these activities go on well into the early hours. The bigger fiestas often finish with spectacular displays of fireworks. Individual villages often have their own fiesta day, so look out for bunting in the streets and ask when the 'big day' is. On the main fiesta days, and away from the main tourist areas, neither shops nor banks will be open. Most main-road petrol stations, however, stay open round the clock.

The following are the main festivals and national holidays:

1 January	New Year
6 January	Dia de los Reyes
January–April	Carnival – events all over the island. Dates vary in each village according to when Easter falls
March/April	Easter – events all over the island
March/April	El Entierro de la Sardina – Ash Wednesday
1 May	Labour Day

30 May	Canary Island Autonomy Day
16 August	The Assumption of the Virgin Mary
September	Fiesta de Nuestra Señora de la Peña
12 October	Spain's National Day
1 November	All Saints' Day
6 December	Constitution Day
8 December	The Immaculate Conception
25 December	Christmas Day

CARNIVAL

Almost every village, town and city hosts its own carnival between January and April every year. The date the festival takes place varies as it depends when Easter falls. Carnival, which often lasts for nine or ten days, is a time to let your hair down and join in with the fun. Many of the floats and groups are imaginatively and elaborately decorated, with flair and care, having taken the whole year to prepare.

The festivities usually start around 17.00, and go on for several hours, depending on the number of floats. The local people tend to make this event an all-night affair with much drinking. Visitors are always welcome to join in, and you will find yourself totally caught up in the exhilarating atmosphere, admiring the ingenuity and inventiveness of the costumes, and infected by the beat of the various bands as they pass. Local shops often sell inexpensive, ready-made costumes, if you don't fancy putting something together for yourself. During Carnival there are excellent professional shows and concerts, most of which are free of charge and open to the public, and funfairs for the children.

DIA DE LOS REYES

This is the first major festival of the year. The Holy Day of the Three Kings takes place on 6 January in Corralejo and the capital, Puerto del Rosario. It is a wonderful occasion during which the three 'kings' parade through the town riding camels, accepting letters from children (similar to the letters that children in Britain send to Father Christmas) and distributing sweets to the spellbound open-eyed youngsters, who wait below with

◆ *Live music creates a fantastic atmosphere during Carnival*

outstretched hands. Most of the small villages also celebrate this fiesta in some way.

EL ENTIERRO DE LA SARDINA

Translated as 'The Burial of the Sardine', this ancient custom started in the mists of time, as a pagan celebration, to symbolise the purging of the bad things that happened during the previous year, and to start afresh. It takes place across the island on Ash Wednesday. The form it takes now is most unusual, with an enormous, beautifully crafted sardine carried on a bier and followed by wailing mourners dressed in funereal colours. The sardine is carried to the beach, and is not in fact buried, but instead is burnt in a huge fire.

FIESTA DE NUESTRA SEÑORA DE LA PEÑA

Fuerteventura's predominant religious festival takes place on the third Saturday in September in **Vega de Río Palmas**, when the rediscovered statue of the Virgen de la Peña is paraded with much solemnity on a litter, carried on the shoulders of selected men. Around the feet of the statue in great profusion are decorations of flowers and candles.

A *romeria* is a pilgrimage, and people from all corners of the island, dressed in local costume, make their way to Vega, singing Canarian folk music accompanied by musicians playing instruments such as the timple, bandurias, laud, mandolin, guitar and violin. There are pauses for traditional dancing (the most famous of which is the polka, originally brought over from Poland), eating and drinking. Home-made food is dispensed to the spectators from hand-woven bags or baskets, and home-brewed drink from leather bottles called *botas*. The women wear enormous hats, not unlike Mexican sombreros (these are made locally from young, bleached palm leaves), and huge black shawls which they prop up on the points of their hats to create a larger degree of shade.

● *Hiring a car will allow you to explore Fuerteventura*

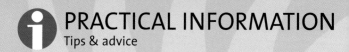
PRACTICAL INFORMATION
Tips & advice

Accommodation

Price ratings are based on a double room for one night.
£ = up to €100   **££** = €100–150   **£££** = over €150

CORRALEJO
Hotel Arena £ A 4-star hotel at great value. 101 rooms, buffet restaurant, swimming pool with poolside bar. Ⓐ Calle El Moro ❶ 928 536 034 Ⓦ www.hotelarenafuerteventura.com

Blue Bay Palace ££ This award-winning hotel is ideally located near the beach, restaurants and shops. The facilities are of a high standard with excellent service and a friendly atmosphere. Ⓐ Avenida Grandes Playas ❶ 928 536 050

Grand Hotel Atlantis Bahia Real £££ A fantastic all-round 5-star hotel offering swimming pools, five restaurants, two bars, exercise classes, bus to beach service, hydrotherapy and other pampering services. You certainly get what you pay for! Ⓐ Avenida Grandes Playas s/n ❶ 928 537 413 Ⓦ www.granhotelatlantisbahiareal.com

PUERTO DEL ROSARIO
Hotel Palace ££ A comfortable and convenient hotel, located on the seafront in central Puerto del Rosario. It has an excellent cafeteria with buffet breakfast and has accommodation suitable for travellers with disabilities. Ⓐ Avenida Maritima 9 ❶ 928 859 464

Hotel Playa Blanca ££ This elegant old hotel was formerly a parador. Located right beside a pretty beach, the rooms are charming with wonderful views. Ⓐ Playa Blanca 45 ❶ 928 851 150

CALETA DE FUSTE
Beach Club Hotel £ At just 2 km (1 mile) from the beach, this 2-star hotel has a great pool and some lovely gardens to stroll around. Hotel guests

are permitted to make full use of the hotel's nearby sister resort, Club Montecastillo. ⓐ Virgen del Carmen ☏ 928 163 620

Hotel Elba Sara ££–£££ One of the island's more upmarket hotels, this 4-star 266-bedroom luxury hotel also has a great restaurant with terrace. ⓐ Golf Resort, Calle Jandía, Km 11 ☏ 928 160 020 ⓔ elbasara@hoteleselba.com

JANDÍA PLAYA

Barceló Jandía Playa ££–£££ Right by Jandía beach and very near Morro del Jable, this large hotel doesn't do things by halves: it has a poolside snack bar, five bars, two restaurants and a disco. There are also four swimming pools, solarium, jacuzzi, childcare facilities and a theatre hall. ⓐ Calle La Mancha, Barranco de Vinamar ☏ 928 547 517

Hotel Riu Palace Jandía ££–£££ Also by Jandía beach, very near Morro del Jable, this 4-star hotel's location is perfect for watersports enthusiasts. There are 209 en-suite rooms, a cocktail bar, restaurant, lounge and jacuzzi. ⓐ Playa Jandía ☏ 928 540 370

COSTA CALMA

Sunrise Monica Beach Hotel ££ Located very near the beach, this 3-star hotel has plenty of sports, leisure and entertainment facilities, 410 rooms, a restaurant and shopping. ⓐ Avenida Jahn Reisen ☏ 928 547 214

Hotel Rio Calma £££ A 4-star hotel, also located near the beach, it has 384 rooms and is six storeys high. There are facilities for childcare, all sorts of pampering treats and a restaurant serving international cuisine. ⓐ Calle Artistas Canarios 8 ☏ 928 546 050

MORRO DEL JABLE

Faro Jandia ££ Excellent facilities, spacious rooms and attractive architecture make this a great choice. ⓐ Avenida de Saladar ☏ 928 545 035

Preparing to go

GETTING THERE

By far the easiest and least expensive way to visit Fuerteventura is on a package holiday. Inclusive packages, operated by all the major travel companies, leave from all over northern Europe several times weekly. You will find tour operators featuring Fuerteventura at ⓦ www.abta.com

For travellers who already have accommodation in Fuerteventura, or wish to book hotels directly, both charter and scheduled airlines sell low-cost direct flights to the island from London and most UK regional airports. Flights from the US go to Puerto del Rosario via Madrid, Spain.

Other search engines for cheap scheduled and charter flights include:
ⓦ www.lastminute.com
ⓦ www.flightline.co.uk
ⓦ www.flydeals.co.uk

The following companies offer cheap flights to Fuerteventura:
Excel Airways (ⓦ www.xl.com): from Manchester, London Gatwick, Glasgow International, Birmingham
Globespan (ⓦ www.flyglobespan.com): from Glasgow International
Ryanair (ⓦ www.ryanair.com): from Liverpool
Thomsonfly (ⓦ www.thomsonfly.com): from Newcastle, Manchester, London Stansted, London Gatwick, Glasgow International, East Midlands, Cardiff, Bristol, Birmingham

Many people are aware that air travel emits CO_2, which contributes to climate change. You may be interested in the possibility of lessening the environmental impact of your flight through the charity Climate Care, which offsets your CO_2 by funding environmental projects around the world. Visit ⓦ www.climatecare.org

TOURISM AUTHORITY

Spanish Tourist Office ⓐ UK office: PO Box 4009, London W1A 6NB
ⓣ 020 7486 8077 ⓕ 020 7486 8034 ⓦ www.spain.info

ⓔ tourspain@latestinfo.co.uk 🕐 09.15–16.15 Mon–Fri ⓐ Republic of Ireland office: PO Box 10015, Dublin 1 🕐 09.15–16.15 Mon–Fri
24-hour brochure request line ❶ UK: 08459 400 180 ❶ Republic of Ireland: 0818 220 290 ❗ Calls are charged at national rates

BEFORE YOU LEAVE

All EU and US citizens are free to travel to Fuerteventura. No inoculations or health preparations are needed. It is a good idea to pack a small first-aid kit to carry with you containing plasters, antiseptic cream, travel-sickness pills, insect repellent and/or bite-relief cream, antihistamine tablets, upset stomach remedies and painkillers. Sun lotion can be more expensive in Fuerteventura than in the UK, so it is worth taking a good selection, especially of the higher-factor lotions if you have children with you, and do not forget after-sun cream as well. If you are taking prescription medicines, ensure that you take enough for the duration of your visit, and an extra copy of the information sheet in case of loss, but you may find it impossible to obtain the same medicines in Fuerteventura.

ENTRY FORMALITIES

The most important documents you will need are your tickets and your passport. Check well in advance that your passport is up to date and has at least three months left to run (six months is even better). All children, including newborn babies, need their own passport. It generally takes at least three weeks to process a passport renewal. This can be longer in the run-up to the summer months. Contact the **Passport Agency** for the latest information on how to renew your passport and the processing times involved. ❶ 0870 521 0410 ⓦ www.ukpa.gov.uk

If you are thinking of hiring a car while you are away, you will need to have your UK driving licence with you. If you want more than one driver for the car, the other drivers must have their licences too. Make sure to bring both parts of the licence.

Insurance

All UK residents are entitled to reduced cost or free medical treatment when temporarily visiting any country within the European Union (EU), including Spain. To obtain this treatment you will need to get a European Health Insurance Card (EHIC) free of charge. The government stresses that the European Health Insurance Card should not be a replacement for travel insurance and it is highly recommended that travellers cover themselves for unexpected costs, including medical emergency repatriation, and the loss of, or damage, to any belongings. For more information, see Ⓦ www.ehic.org.uk

MONEY

The currency in the Canaries is the same as in mainland Spain: the euro, with one euro broken down into 100 cents or *centimos*. Notes come in denominations of €5, €10, €20, €50, €100, €200 and €500. Coins are available in denominations of €1, €2 and 1, 2,5, 10, 20 and 50 cents. You will need some currency before you go, especially if your flight gets you to your destination at the weekend or late in the day after the banks have closed. Traveller's cheques are the safest way to carry money because the money will be refunded if the cheques are lost or stolen. You can exchange money at the airport before you depart. You should also make sure that your credit, charge and debit cards are up to date – you do not want them to expire mid-holiday – and that your credit limit is sufficient to allow you to make those holiday purchases. Once you arrive, you will find cash dispensers in all the resorts.

CLIMATE

Daytime temperatures do not vary greatly throughout the year, around 19°C (66°F) in Fuerteventura, although there is light rain sometimes. Almost all the rain falls in the winter, but even in the wettest months (December/January) rainfall totals average only 2.7 cm (just over 1 in) per month. However, it can be chilly in the evenings during the winter months, so it is advisable to take something warmer for the evenings.

Be sure that young children wear something on their heads, because the UV rays are strong and there is often a strong breeze on the island, making the sun feel deceptively cooler than it actually is.

BAGGAGE ALLOWANCE

Baggage allowances vary according to the airline, destination and class of travel, but 15–20 kg (33–44 lb) per person is the norm for luggage that is carried in the hold (it usually tells you what the weight limit is on your ticket). You are also allowed one item of cabin baggage usually weighing no more than 5 kg (11 lb), though some airlines allow 10 kg (22 lb) and measuring 46 by 30 by 23 cm (18 by 12 by 9 in). In addition, you can usually carry your duty-free purchases, umbrella, handbag, coat, camera, etc. as hand baggage. Large items – surfboards, golf clubs, collapsible wheelchairs and pushchairs – are usually charged as extras and it is a good idea to let the airline know in advance if you want to bring these.

During your stay

AIRPORTS

The international airport in Fuerteventura is a modern and impressive building. It is situated very close to the capital, Puerto del Rosario, and only ten minutes by car from the resort of Caleta de Fuste. Flights mainly arrive from Europe and other Canary islands, with over four million passengers passing through every year. You can get to and from the airport by taxi, which can be found directly outside Arrivals, or by coach transfer if travelling on a package tour. There are also two bus routes serving the airport. The main Fuerteventura airport bus leaves every 30 minutes and runs between Puerto del Rosario and Caleta de Fuste. The second airport bus is not as frequent and runs between the capital and Morro del Jable, in the south of the island.

COMMUNICATIONS

TELEPHONING FUERTEVENTURA

Fuerteventura is essentially an area of Spain. Dial 34 for Spain, followed by 928, which is the Fuerteventura area code, followed by the six-digit number.

TELEPHONING ABROAD

The dialling code for international access is 00. Follow this by the country code (UK 44, US and Canada 1, Australia 61, New Zealand 64, South Africa 27, Republic of Ireland 353) and then the area code minus the initial 0. The cheapest time to call home is after 20.00 on Saturday and all day Sunday.

Phone booths Most phone booths in Fuerteventura have multilingual instructions. You can buy international phonecards in most shops. To use a public phone, first lift the receiver and wait for a tone and for a display asking you to introduce money or a card. Insert coins or a card, and then push the numbered buttons to dial. When you have

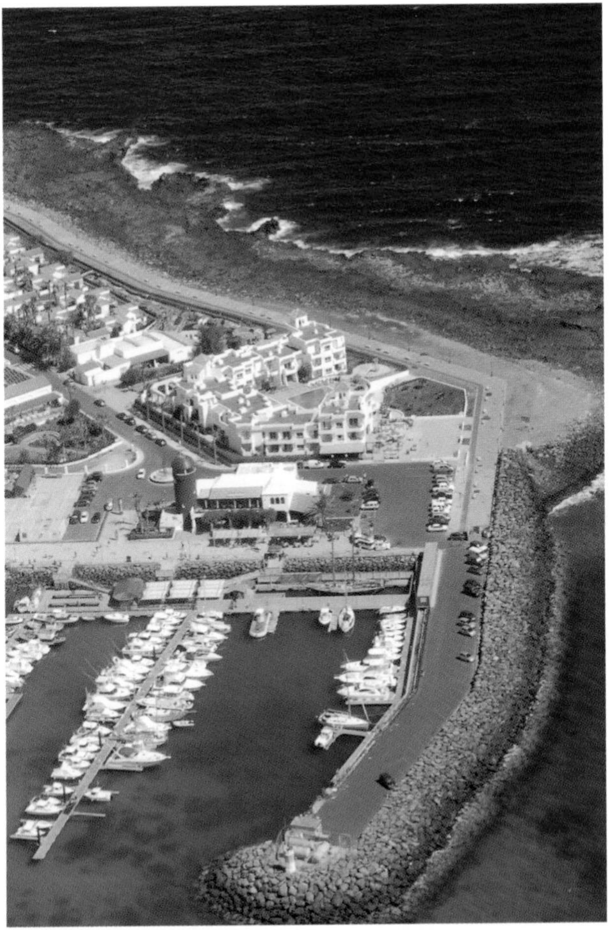

Puerto del Rosario harbour

finished you may get some change or the card will be returned with unused credits.

Post The postal service in Spain is called *correos*. You'll find large branches in the major towns, which generally open all day Monday to Saturday. Smaller branches in outlying towns and villages may only be open in the morning. Post boxes in Fuerteventura are bright yellow.

Internet There are now internet cafés in most towns; many have broadband.

CUSTOMS

As a rule the people of Fuerteventura follow many of the same day-to-day customs as people in the rest of Spain, especially in terms of how they relate to one another. Generally they are sociable and greet and say goodbye to strangers in public places. When they are introduced they shake hands, and women will kiss one another on each cheek. Close friends and family members often kiss when they meet and say goodbye. People also often follow quite a rigid order to their day, starting work early, taking a long lunch and often a siesta, followed by a return to work or meeting friends for tea or an early evening drink. Dinner will invariably be late. It's always a good idea to try to adapt to the local traditions and rhythms of the day, as you will get more out of your stay.

DRESS CODES

The islanders are basically Catholic, and have been hurtled into modern living over the last 60 years, so it is respectful to them not to go into the bigger towns such as Puerto del Rosario wearing skimpy shorts and tops, or shirtless. This dress code is absolutely fine for the holiday resorts.

ELECTRICITY

The islands have the same voltage as the UK, but with two-pin plugs, so you will need to bring an adaptor. These are readily available in the UK at electrical shops or major chemists. If you are considering buying electrical appliances to take home, always check that they will work in the UK before you buy them.

EMERGENCIES

The **British Consulate Las Palmas** on the island of Gran Canaria is the nearest British consul. ⓐ Consular Section, Calle Luis Morote 6 – 3rd floor, Las Palmas de Gran Canaria, Canary Islands ⓣ 928 262 508 ⓕ 928 267 774 ⓦ www.britishembassy.gov.uk/spain

GETTING AROUND

Car hire and driving The police are very kind, understanding and helpful, but they are very firm, so do uphold the law. As in the UK, drinking and driving is severely dealt with. The driver and all passengers must wear a seat belt. Children under ten must travel in the back of the car. Never park where you should not – yellow lines mean 'do not park here' – since they are very quick to tow you away. They have special vehicles called *gruas*, which take the car to a designated place, normally difficult to find, and of course you have to pay to get it back. Never cross a solid line when on a slip road joining a main road – make sure you wait until you get to the dotted line part before filtering in. Remember to give way to

EMERGENCY NUMBERS

General emergency and ambulance ⓣ 112
Police ⓣ 091
Fire Brigade ⓣ 080
Guardia Civil emergency number ⓣ 062

Guardia Civil local numbers:
Puerto del Rosario ⓣ 928 850 503
Morro del Jable ⓣ 928 541 107
Gran Tarajal ⓣ 928 162 755

National Police:
Puerto del Rosario ⓣ 928 855 100

Puerto del Rosario General Hospital ⓣ 928 531 799

traffic coming from your left when you are on a roundabout, and to go round it anticlockwise. If your car uses unleaded petrol, you need *gasolina sin plomo*.

Car hire in Spain and its islands has become increasingly competitive. Before you go check out the various price-comparison websites for the best deals. Once on the island, shop around the local companies – even in high season you'll find they are in serious competition with each other. Some companies will take a deposit to cover any insurance excess if the car is damaged. Some will also charge you for a tank of petrol, while others will not charge you for fuel, but will expect the car to be returned full. When collecting the car you will need to present both parts of your driving licence and a valid credit card, usually the one you booked the car with.

Rules of the road Remember to drive on the right. Motorists must carry their driving licences, passports and car-hire documents at all times. Failure to do so will result in an automatic on-the-spot fine if you are stopped in one of the frequent road checks.

Roads In general, the road surfaces are good. Road markings are clear, but some of the traffic systems can be confusing when first encountered. Be aware that traffic priorities in these complex traffic systems do not always conform to your expectations: you might find a stop sign part-way around a roundabout or even on a motorway.

Petrol This is inexpensive on the islands and petrol stations are frequent along main routes. Always fill up with petrol before heading off into the hills or the interior.

Parking Parking meters are usual in built-up or popular areas. Here the parking spaces are marked out in blue. Pay at the meter and display the ticket on the windscreen. Parking in side streets is generally allowed

SPEED LIMITS
- Autovia (primary road) 100 km/h (62 mph)
- Carretera (A road) 80 km/h (50 mph)
- Built-up areas 40 km/h (25 mph)

except where the kerbstones are painted yellow (or green and white in bus-stop areas). Illegal parking results in the car being towed away.

Useful words for drivers
- *aparcamiento* parking
- *estacionamiento prohibido* no parking
- *ceda al paso* give way to the right and left
- *circunvalación* ring road

Public transport Current bus timetables are available from tourist offices. A regular and reliable bus service operates on the island. Like the spokes of a wheel, buses mostly operate directly into and out of the capital. This means a change of bus is often necessary to reach a particular destination. It pays to be on the early side since buses sometimes run marginally ahead of schedule. Not all services operate on Sunday. The Canarian word for bus, *guagua*, is pronounced 'wah-wah'. The main resorts are connected to the capital, with a frequent bus service, mostly half hourly.

Taxis Official taxis are easily recognised by the sign on the roof. Next to the sign is a light that shows green when the taxi is free. Generally, short journeys within town are not expensive, especially with four people sharing. The taxis are colour coded according to the district in which they operate. For longer journeys you should agree a price in advance.

Ferries and hydrofoils A complex network of inter-island ferries and hydrofoils links the seven main islands of the Canaries, and schedules change very regularly, so you need to check times locally. Most of the inter-island services are operated by **Trasmediterranea** ⓦ www.trasmediterranea.es (in Spanish only) or the **Fred Olsen Express Line**. Timetable details and online booking on: ⓦ www.fredolsen.es (in Spanish only). The local airline, **Binter Canarias**, provides regular flights between the islands. Booking centre ☎ 902 391 392 ⓦ www.bintercanarias.es

HEALTH, SAFETY & CRIME

Chemists Easily recognised by the big green cross above the door with the word *Farmacia*, chemists are very good on the islands, supplying everything you might need including antibiotics, which you can buy over the counter. The staff are always very helpful and knowledgeable – if you want something that they do not have in stock, they will normally get it for you very quickly.

Health hazards The sun is very strong at all times of the year so take great care with sunbathing, even when there is a cool breeze. Use high-factor creams initially and limit your sunbathing hours. Cover up at midday and in the early afternoon when the sun is at its highest. Remember, a slow tan is deeper and lasts longer. Do not let sunburn ruin your holiday!

Water Tap water is produced by desalination. It is not unsafe but does not taste good and is rich in minerals, which can cause upset stomachs. It is recommended that you drink bottled water.

Clinics All resorts have clinics where English is spoken, so if you have minor ailments or injuries it is often better and faster to go to one of these, rather than to the hospital emergency department. All have fully qualified doctors and nursing staff. However, they may not be able to accept your EHIC or equivalent and treatment will have to be paid for.

Security In a hotel, if all else fails and you cannot get a complaint sorted out to your satisfaction, ask for the complaints book (*el libro de reclamaciones*). Hotels are required by law to have one – you write down your complaint and it will be forwarded to the Spanish Ministry of Tourism.

Crime prevention Take as much care of your personal property as you would at home. Watch out for pickpockets, especially in crowded market places. Crime with violence is unusual, but do not take risks. Leave nothing of value in a parked car, not even locked in the boot. Bag snatchers are around, too, so carry your valuables in a bag securely anchored to your body.

Lost property Report any loss or theft to your holiday representative. If an insurance claim is to be made, you must report thefts within 24 hours to the Municipal Police or Guardia Civil, from whom an official report must be obtained.

Police If you have a problem – say with lost or stolen property – talk to your holiday representative or hotel desk; they can help you make an official statement to the police. There are basically two types of police force on the island: La Policia Municipal, who come under the local authority at the Town Hall (Ayuntamiento), are responsible for the law and order in the local authority area and also traffic control. They wear dark blue uniforms. The other kind are La Guardia Civil (Civil Guard) and they are responsible for law and order in the rural areas, and traffic control on main roads and cities. If you are committing an offence while driving, they are the ones that will stop and fine you. They wear green uniforms.

◓ The island's beaches are particularly clean

MEDIA

There is one English newspaper in Fuerteventura, *Fuertenews*, which is published in Corralejo. Local radio stations include Power FM which broadcasts across the Canaries between 91 and 92 MHz. QFM broadcasts on 98 MHz. These days, if you want serious news you can access the BBC World Service online. It's also possible, if you have access to some digital packages, to watch EuroNews, a pan-European magazine-style news programme. Coming from France – the adverts are in French – it broadcasts in different European languages simultaneously, and whether you can get the English version will depend on the settings on the digital receiver.

OPENING HOURS

General shopping hours are 09.00–13.00 and 17.00–20.00. Sunday is a general closing day. Shopping hours are not rigidly followed, especially in tourist areas. Supermarkets and bakeries often open earlier, usually at 08.30, and there are always some which stay open all day. Many shops relying on tourism stay open until late evening, closing at around 22.00.

RELIGION

Spain is a Catholic country, and Fuerteventura is no exception. You should bear in mind that in some places certain behaviour is inappropriate. You shouldn't wear a swimming costume to wander around a church, for example. If you want to attend Mass, services are usually on Saturday afternoon or Sunday morning. In smaller, more remote towns and villages the church is still very much at the heart of village life and it's only polite to respect this, however it manifests itself.

TIME DIFFERENCES

There is no time difference between the Canaries and the UK. The clocks go forward in March and back in October simultaneously.

TIPPING

As a tourist you would probably be expected to tip around ten per cent. However, in less touristy places you'll notice that the Spanish often don't tip to a formula, but instead round up to the nearest euro or five euros, depending on the size of the bill and what coins and notes are being used. If you tip too much, the local Spanish may think you're being a bit of a big shot! You may hear the word *capitalista*.

TOILETS

The days of finding a grubby pissoir out the back of a restaurant are generally over. Most bars and restaurants in Spain as a whole now have clean and modern bathrooms.

TRAVELLERS WITH DISABILITIES

Spain's commitment to people with disabilities has been second to none over the last decade or two. You'll find that museums and other public buildings will often have facilities to cater for the needs of visitors with a disability. Spain's national association for the disabled, the Confederación Coordinadora Estatal de Minusválidos Físicos de España (COCEMFE), has a travel company, Servi-COCEMFE, based in Madrid, that provides information for travellers with a disability to Spain as a whole.
🕾 914 138 001

Europe For All An excellent new online information service for travellers with disabilities within Europe. Ⓦ www.europeforall.com

RADAR The principal UK forum and pressure group for people with disabilities. ⓐ 12 City Forum, 250 City Road, London EC1V 8AF
🕾 020 7250 3222 Ⓦ www.radar.org.uk

SATH (Society for Accessible Travel & Hospitality) Advises US-based travellers with disabilities. ⓐ 347 Fifth Ave, Suite 610, New York, NY 10016
🕾 212 447 7284 Ⓦ www.sath.org

◯ *Jandía Peninsula. Fuerteventura's scenery attracts many tourists*

FIND THE LATEST HOTSPOT

Get more from your holiday and find out the best restaurants, bars, beaches and family-friendly attractions from our handy pocket guides. Our wide range covers up to 45 destinations:

Algarve
Bali
Bulgaria
Corfu
Corsica
Costa Blanca
Costa Brava & Costa Dorada
Costa del Sol & Costa de Almeria
Côte D'Azur
Crete
Croatia
Cuba
Cyprus
Dominican Republic
Egypt
Fuerteventura
Gibraltar
Goa
Gran Canaria
Guernsey
Ibiza
Ionian Islands
Jamaica

Jersey
Lanzarote
Madeira
Mallorca
Malta
Menorca
Mexico
Morocco
Neapolitan Riviera
Orlando
Rhodes & Kos
Santorini
Sardinia
Sicily
Sri Lanka
Tenerife
Thailand
Tunisia
Turkey –
  Aegean Coast
  Lycian Coast
  Mediterranean Coast

Available from all good bookshops, your local Thomas Cook travel store or browse and buy on-line at www.thomascookpublishing.com

ACKNOWLEDGEMENTS

We would like to thank all the photographers, picture libraries and organisations for the loan of the photographs reproduced in this book, to whom copyright in the photograph belongs:

Alamy Images pages 74 & 95 (Lyndon Beddoe), pages 26 & 70 (Alan Copson City Pictures), page 63 (Jean Dominique Dallet), page 29 (Cris Haigh), page 105 (John Henshall), pages 53 & 67 (Isifa Image Service s.r.o), page 16 (Nicholas Pitt); Photoinsel/Dreamstime (page 115); World Pictures/Photoshot (pages 13, 22, 42, 51, 60, 80); Pictures Colour Library (pages 57, 76–7, 101, 107, 124); age fotostock/SuperStock (pages 10–11, 44, 85); Thomas Cook Tour Operations (pages 1, 5, 19, 21, 34, 38, 65, 83, 92, 98, 121); Tips Images/Arco Digital Images (page 87); Wikimedia Commons/Michael Sanders (page 48).

Project editor: Alison Coupe
Layout: Donna Pedley
Proofreader: Janet McCann
Indexer: Karolin Thomas

Send your thoughts to
books@thomascook.com

- Found a beach bar, peaceful stretch of sand or must-see sight that we don't feature?

- Like to tip us off about any information that needs a little updating?

- Want to tell us what you love about this handy little guidebook and more importantly how we can make it even handier?

Then here's your chance to tell all! Send us ideas, discoveries and recommendations today and then look out for your valuable input in the next edition of this title.

Email to the above address or write to:
HotSpots Series Editor, Thomas Cook Publishing, PO Box 227, Coningsby Road, Peterborough PE3 8SB, UK.

Any feeling that had existed between Davina and Ruy de Silvadores, her husband and the father of her son, had long since turned to ashes—and it was only for her child's sake that Davina was now going back to Spain, to her husband and his aristocratic family. She was ready for a difficult time—but she had not anticipated the situation that awaited her . . .

THE CAGED TIGER

TIGER

BY

PENNY JORDAN

MILLS & BOON LIMITED
15-16 BROOK'S MEWS
LONDON W1A 1DR

First published 1982
Australian copyright 1982
Philippine copyright 1982
This edition 1982

© Penny Jordan 1982

ISBN 0 263 73845 0

Set in Monophoto Plantin 10 on 11½ pt.
01/06/82 – 53903

*Made and printed in Great Britain by
Richard Clay (The Chaucer Press) Ltd,
Bungay, Suffolk*

CHAPTER ONE

IT would be evening before the plane landed in Seville.
It had been the only flight she had been able to get at
such short notice and during the height of the season.
It had been cheaper too, because of a sudden cancella-
tion, but it had been a long day—all that hanging
around at Heathrow to make sure they got the seats.
She pushed a slim pale hand through her silver-blonde
weight of hair, her amethyst eyes clouding as she
shifted Jamie's baby weight from one arm to the other.
Baby ... She stifled a small smile. At three he considered himself a very grown-up young man. She often
had difficulty convincing people that she was actually
his mother—not just because she looked younger than
her twenty-four years. Her small, slender body looked
far too fragile to ever have carried a child. But it had.
She wasn't a fool; she knew that despite the plain gold
wedding ring she wore people wondered if she had
actually ever been married—if Jamie was not simply
the result of a youthful indiscretion. They were wrong,
though. She had most emphatically been married; had
had a husband ... There were still faint traces of his
orange juice round Jamie's mouth, and as she reached
into her pocket for a tissue the letter crackled
ominously.

She didn't need to take it out, to look at the heavy,
expensive crested paper again. Every word written on
it was engraved upon her heart, and had been agonised
over ever since the letter arrive a fortnight ago.

Only a fortnight? It felt more like years. The letter

5

was brief, couched in words as dry as dust, making it impossible for her to think it had been written with any feeling. But then it hadn't. Any feeling that had ever existed between Jamie's father and herself had long since turned to ashes.

So what was she doing on this plane, flying back to Spain, taking her son to his unknown father?

She glanced down quickly at the sleeping child. Under the baby plumpness lay even now the signs of his recent illness. Enteritis was so frightening in a child—one could do nothing but hope and pray. He was over it now, the doctors assured her, but she was haunted by the fear that another poor summer would lower his resistance to the point where he would be ill again come winter. In Spain he would thrive in the warmth and luxury which were his birthright; his skin would take on the mahogany hue of his father's, his hair would gleam blue-black as a raven's wing in the strong sunshine . . . Hair that reminded her unbearably at times of Ruy . . . She stroked it back from his forehead where it had fallen in unruly curls. Even in sleep his profile had a subconscious arrogance inherited from a long line of Spanish hidalgos . . .

She had done her best for him, but it could never come anywhere near to matching what Ruy could give him. She was lucky in that she had been able to work from home, but her illustrations for children's books and cards did not bring in enough to keep them in luxury, nor to provide the winter away from the English climate which the doctor had suggested might be as well.

Jamie stirred in his sleep, the almost purple eyes which were what she had passed on to him remaining tightly closed. She had always been honest with him.

When she thought he was old enough to understand she had explained that his daddy lived far away in another country, without going into too much detail. He had been curious, but had accepted her matter-of-fact explanations without evincing any surprise or distress. At play-school several of the other children lived alone with their mothers, and he saw nothing odd in their own aloneness. Which was wrong, something inside her told her, as she remembered her own parents' happy marriage. If a child did not grow up knowing that love could exist between adults of both sexes then how could he in turn pass that knowledge on to his own children?

She was being sentimental, she warned herself. Jamie was unlikely to learn anything good about human relationships from observing hers with his father. Which brought her thoughts back full circle. Why had Ruy written to her? Why did he want his son—now?

She had been so sure when she left that he would find some way of having their marriage set aside—it had been a Catholic ceremony in accordance with his religion, but his family were influential and rich, and there were always ways and means . . . His mother had never liked the marriage. 'Liked!' She almost laughed. It would have been truer to say that her mother-in-law detested her, if one could apply such a word to the ice-cold contempt the Condesa de Silvadores had evinced each time their paths had crossed—and they had been many. The Condesa had seen to that. In the end a million tiny pinpricks could be more fatal than one crippling blow.

The plane landed, and a smiling stewardess helped her with Jamie. 'He's gorgeous,' she commented as she

held him so that Davina could collect all their posses-
sions, 'but not a bit like you.'

'No, he takes after his father,' Davina answered
briefly, trying not to let her voice falter.

The stewardess could not know what the words had
cost her. How much it always cost her to admit how
much Jamie resembled his father—the father who had
never wanted him, who had never seen him; never once
sent him a birthday or Christmas present, made no
attempts whatsoever to see him—until now. And even
now he had left it to his mother—the woman who had
always derided and scorned her—to write the letter
summoning her back to the Palacio de los Naranjos—
the Palace of the Orange Trees—the home of the
Silvadores family set amongst the orange groves from
which the family's fortune was derived and whose scent
hung sharply and sweetly on the early morning air.

A shiver trembled through her, and mistaking it for
coldness, the stewardess touched her arm, motioning
her towards the airport building. Despite the huge
number of people who passed through her life daily,
something about Davina intrigued the other girl. She
looked so frail, spiritual almost, her beauty tinged with
a contemplative acceptance that touched the heart far
more than any more overt signs of grief. What had
happened to her to give her that look? She might have
posed for some great painter of the Renaissance. Her
expression told of great suffering and resignation, and
yet surely she had all the things any woman could
want? Youth, beauty, this adorable baby, and somewhere the man who had loved her enough to give her
his son.

When they emerged from the Customs hall it was
dark. Davina walked out into the soft silkiness of the

Spanish night, Jamie in her arms. Spain! How the scents of the night brought back memories. Herself and Ruy wandering hand in hand through the orange groves during their honeymoon, and later, when the moon had risen fully and he had taken her so paganly in that shadowed garden, teaching her and thrilling her until her passion matched his. She had been happy then—deliriously happy, but she had paid for it later. She had thought Ruy loved her, had never realised that to him she was merely a substitute for the girl he had really loved; that he had married her to punish that girl.

In the shadowed garden of his home she had thought she had found Paradise. But every Eden must have a serpent and hers had held Ruy's mother, the woman who hated her so much that she had deliberately opened her eyes to the truth.

And now Ruy wanted her back—no, not her; it was his son. The only one he was ever likely to have, or so the letter had told her. Jamie was his heir, and his place was with his father, learning all that he must learn if he was to take it successfully. And Davina could not deny it, although she could not understand why Ruy had not been able to get his freedom— Freedom to marry the girl he had loved all along, the girl he had really wanted to be the mother of the son who would succeed him, as Silvadores had succeeded Silvadores in an unbroken line from the sixteenth century onwards.

The letter had said that she would be collected from the airport. A porter brought her cases and she smiled as she tipped him. His eyes rested appreciatively on her face, and her hair, like spun silver, and so very different from the girls of his own race. Her features were patrician and perfect, her lips chiselled and firm, her complexion as fine as porcelain, her huge amethyst eyes fringed with luxuriously thick dark lashes.

She was the most beautiful thing he had ever seen, Ruy had once told her. But he hadn't meant it.

'Davina?'

She hadn't heard the opulent Mercedes drive up nor seen its driver emerge to come and touch her lightly on the arm, and she spun round, startled, her eyes widening slightly as she found herself looking into a face she remembered as being a boy's.

'Sebastian?'

'Let me take the boy. He looks heavy.' Her brother-in-law lifted Jamie from her arms with a competence which would have amused her four years ago. Then he had been nineteen, and still at the university studying viticulture in preparation for taking over the family's vineyards. Now, at twenty-three, he had matured considerably. Although superficially he resembled his brother, Sebastian lacked Ruy's totally male grace. Where Ruy was lean and muscled Sebastian showed a tendency towards what would develop into plumpness in middle years. He was not as tall as Ruy, his features nowhere near as tautly chiselled, but for all that he was still a very handsome young man. Especially when he smiled—which he had been doing as he held his small nephew. However, the moment he turned towards Davina the smile was replaced by cool formality. She was ushered into the expensive car as though she were a complete stranger, her luggage stowed in the boot, and then Sebastian was sliding into the driver's seat and starting the engine. It surprised Davina that if one of the brothers had to meet her, it had not been Ruy. Surely he must be anxious to see his son to permit his mother to write demanding their presence?

She voiced her opinion of her husband's lack of manners as they drove out of the city. In the driving mirror Sebastian's eyes met hers, before moving away evasively. She remembered that he had always hero-worshipped his elder brother. Twelve years separated them, and Ruy had already been a man while Sebastian was still a child in school.

'He was unable to meet you,' was all the explanation Sebastian would vouchsafe, and Davina was glad she had played down the meeting with his father to Jamie. The little boy would have been sadly disappointed had he been expecting him at the airport. In point of fact Davina was surprised that Sebastian had come for them. She had half expected to be collected by the family chauffeur, rather like a piece of unwanted luggage.

Before her marriage to the Conde de Silvadores Ruy's mother had lived in South America, the only daughter of a wealthy industrialist, and had been brought up very strictly. She had never learned to drive and was always taken wherever she wished to go by a chauffeur. That had been yet another cause of dissent between them. Davina had found it very hard to adjust to being the wife of a rich nobleman without having to behave like some Victorian heroine, not permitted to put a foot out of doors without an escort. Used to running her own life and relatively untrammelled freedom, she had rebelled against the strictures Ruy's mother had wanted to impose upon her.

Her small sigh brought Sebastian's eyes to her face. She was very beautiful, this silver-haired girl who had married his adored brother—even more beautiful now than she had been when they married. Then she had been merely a girl; now she was a woman ... His eyes rested on his brother's child. Madre would be well pleased. The boy was all Silvadores.

Unaware of her brother-in-law's covert inspection, Davina stared out into the dusk of a Spanish evening, forgotten memories surfacing like so many pieces of flotsam, things she had vowed never to remember filling her mind, like the vivid beauty of the sunset, the subtle smell of oranges on the evening air, peasants trudging contentedly homewards after a day in the fields, donkeys with panniers laden. She sighed.

The Palacio lay between Seville and Cordoba, and this journey was the very first she had taken with Ruy after their marriage. They had left Barcelona straight away after the ceremony and flown to Seville ...

More to bring a halt to her errant thoughts than out of any real curiosity, she questioned Sebastian about his life since she had left.

Yes, he had now left the university, he answered politely, and was running the family's vineyards. Davina had a hazy recollection of a young Spanish girl whom his mother had wished him to marry, and when she mentioned her Sebastian told her that they had been married for two years. 'But, alas, without any little ones,' he volunteered sadly. 'The doctors say that Rosita will probably never have children. An operation to remove her appendix caused some complications...' He shrugged philosophically, and Davina's heart went out to his young wife. She knew all too well what importance was placed on the bearing of children—especially sons—in her husband's family. Hadn't she had it drummed into her time and time again by her mother-in-law that Silvadores had been linked with the history of Spain for hundreds of years and how important it was for the name to continue?

Now she could understand why the family were so anxious for Jamie to be brought up in the full knowledge of what his role would one day be, although previously she had always expected, when Ruy had their marriage set aside so that he could marry Carmelita, that Jamie would be disinherited in favour of the sons she would bear him. She was not au fait with the Spanish inheritance laws, nor had she made any attempt to be. She had left Ruy swearing that never would she ask him for a single penny towards his son's upbringing, and she had stuck rigorously to that vow, and at the first suggestion that she had come to Spain with any thought of material gain, she would leave at once. They were the ones who wanted Jamie. All she wanted for her son was his restored health, and had there been any other means of achieving it she would have gladly taken them. She had no wish to be indebted to her husband or his family, but as the solicitor she had gone to see in England had gently pointed out, there was a possibility that Ruy might appeal to the Spanish courts to have custody of Jamie given to him, and as the child was his heir they might very well grant it.

With that threat hanging over her Davina had had no choice but to comply with the terms of the letter. That way at least she would still be able to be with her child.

They were starting to climb, driving towards the Sierra de los Santos. High up in those mountains was a monastery which had once belonged to the monks of the Inquisition, and she shivered as she remembered Ruy telling her about the ancestor of his who had been to England with Philip of Spain and fallen in love there with one of Queen Elizabeth's ladies in waiting. He had married his English Rose, as he had named his bride, and carried her back to Spain with him, but despite the fact that Jane Carfax was of the same religion as himself, the priests of the Inquisition had insisted that in reality she was an English spy. They had demanded that Cristo hand over his wife so that she could be questioned, but the Spaniard knew too much about their torture chambers to relinquish his wife. Instead he had made secret plans to leave his country with his bride and start a new life far beyond the reach of the burning fires to which the priests wished to sacrifice his love.

On the very night they were to leave for the coast the house had been surrounded and they had been taken to the monastery. Their secret had been betrayed by Cristo's brother, and the two young lovers had perished together in the flames. The brother himself had died shortly after, after an agonising illness—punishment from God, the villagers had called it. The story had haunted Davina. And now, as she raised her eyes to the black bulk of the mountains she shivered, holding Jamie tightly.

'Soon be there,' Sebastian told her over his shoulder. 'Everything is in readiness for you. Madre has given you your own suite of rooms. She has engaged a nurse for the little one. She will help him to learn Spanish, although he is not yet old enough for formal lessons, but he must learn his father's tongue . . .'

How much they took for granted, these arrogant Spaniards! Davina thought resentfully. Already her mother-in-law seemed to be usurping her place. Well, she would soon learn that Davina was no shy, awkward girl now, eager to please and terrified. Jamie was her

child, and she would be the one to say what he would
and would not learn.

And yet half an hour later when the Mercedes
stopped in the courtyard of the beautiful Moorish
house which had been the home of her husband's
family for centuries, and Sebastian took the sleeping
child in his arms, she had to admit that when it came
to loving children, Englishmen could learn a good deal
from their Spanish counterparts. As they walked towards the house Jamie stirred, and half frightened that
he would think she had left him, Davina darted forward to take his hand. Two dimples appeared in his
chubby cheeks as he smiled, his arms extended towards
her. As she took him from Sebastian, she buried her
face in the small baby neck, suddenly overwhelmed by
dread, by the fear that she had done the wrong thing.

Too many memories that were best left dead had
been stirred already. She might be able to close her
heart against her husband, but she could not close her
mind to her memories ... Memories of the very first
time she had seen this house; of how she had been
entranced by Ruy's casual explanation that it had once
been the home of a Moorish prince and that much of
the original architecture remained. Even now she could
hear the music of the fountains playing in the courtyard
which had once been the sole property of the ladies of
the harem, and even before the massive wooden doors
opened, already in her mind's eye she could see the
gracious hallway with its mosaic-tiled floor and elegant
Moorish architecture. Everything was the same—but
different. Then she had arrived with a husband she
had thought loved her as totally as she loved him. This
time she arrived with her son—the product of that
union.

The doors opened, and in the light from the chandeliers Davina saw her mother-in-law waiting to greet them, regal and feminine in one of the long hostess gowns she always wore in the evening—always black, always elegant. How intimidated she had been on the first occasion! But not this time. Oh, definitely not this time.

Her head held high, she stepped past Sebastian and into the house. Her mother-in-law's eyes flickered once as Davina greeted her and then went straight to Jamie with a hunger no amount of sophistication could hide. She held out her arms, but Davina did not place Jamie into them. He was busily staring around his new surroundings.

'So this is Ruy's child.'

Davina ignored the other woman's emotion, her eyes hard as they probed the shadows of the room, as she forced herself to damp down the feeling nothing would make her admit was disappointment.

Sebastian had walked into the *salón*, plainly expecting that they would follow him. Her mother-in-law indicated that Davina should precede her into the room, and with her legs trembling a little Davina did so.

The room was much as she remembered. Rich Persian carpets glowed on the floor, the antique furniture was still as highly polished as it had always been, the room looking more like a film set than someone's home, and her heart sank at the thought of condemning Jamie to a house where his inquisitive little fingers would be forbidden to touch and explore.

A small, slight girl in a demure cotton dress stood up as they walked in. Davina guessed at once that she was Sebastian's wife, Rosita, and this was confirmed when Sebastian introduced her. Like her mother-in-law, Rosita's eyes went immediately to the child in Davina's arms, and she turned to her husband whispering something huskily in Spanish.

'She says that the child very much resembles Ruy,' Sebastian explained to Davina.

'I know.'

Davina could see that the dry words had surprised them. She had not been able to speak Spanish when she married Ruy, and as he spoke excellent English she had only made a halfhearted attempt to learn. But during the lonely weeks after her return to England she had bought herself some foreign language tapes, partially to pass the time, and partially because then she still hoped that it had all been a mistake and that Ruy loved her and would come to take her home. To her own surprise she had shown quite a facility for the language, and could now speak it reasonably well. She could tell by her mother-in-law's expression that the older woman thought her knowledge of her language had been gained purely to impress them, and to show her exactly how little she cared what they thought about her she lifted her chin proudly and said coolly:

'I was given to understand that Ruy was anxious to see his son. Where is he? Out somewhere with Carmelita?'

Rosita paled and started to tremble. Sebastian gripped her hand, his mouth white, and only the Condesa appeared unmoved by her question. What was she supposed to do? Pretend ignorance? Pretend that she didn't know that her husband loved someone else?

Before anyone could speak Davina heard an unfamiliar sound in the hall. For a moment it reminded her of her own days spent pushing Jamie's pram, which was quite ridiculous, for who would push a pram through the immaculate rooms of this house?

The *salón* had double doors, both of which stood open. All three members of the Silvadores family were staring towards them with varying degrees of tension evident in their faces. Only Davina's expression was openly puzzled. Sebastian walked towards her, his hand touching her arm, as though he wanted to say something, but before he could do so Davina knew the reason why her husband had not met her at the airport but had sent his brother instead. For the sound she had heard was made by a wheelchair and in it, his face drawn in tight lines of pain, was Ruy.

CHAPTER TWO

'RUY!'

His name burst past her lips of its own volition in a shocked gasp, *his* expression going from sheer incredulity to bitter anger as he stared from her slender body, half hidden by the child in her arms, to the faces of his relatives.

'*Madre de Dios!*' he swore angrily, his nostrils pinched and white with the force of his rage. 'What kind of conspiracy is this? What is going on?' he demanded harshly. 'What is *she* doing here?'

If she had felt shocked before, it was nothing to what she was feeling now, Davina admitted, her face going as white as his, but before she could say anything, Ruy's mother was speaking.

'She has come because I requested her to,' she told her son, holding his eyes coolly.

Davina wasn't paying much attention to them. She was still too stunned by the fact that this was actually Ruy, the proud and strong, in a wheelchair, to appreciate the full enormity of what her mother-in-law had done.

'*You* requested it?' The thin nostrils dilated further. 'By whose authority?' he demanded softly. 'I am still master in my own house, Madre. I can still say who may and may not rest under its roof, even if I can no longer walk as other men, but must needs propel myself about like a babe in arms.'

With his rage directed at his mother, Davina was

able to study him properly for the first time. What she saw shocked her. The Ruy whom she had known had walked tall—a veritable god among men, and if she was honest she would have to admit that she had thrilled to the arrogant grace; the hint of ruthless mastery cloaked by modern civilisation like velvet covering tempered steel. Now there were deep lines of pain scored from nose to mouth which were new to her, and a bitterness in the dark eyes that made Jamie cry out protestingly as her arms tightened round him unthinkingly.

His cry brought Ruy's eyes to them in scorching denunciation; a look that stripped her of everything and left her aching with a need to escape from it.

He turned his chair abruptly so that she was faced with the sight of his dark head.

'Get her out of here,' he told his mother emotionlessly. 'I never want to set eyes on her again.'

'And your son?'

His mother said the words so quietly that Davina couldn't believe that he had heard them, never mind stopped. But he had, and he turned his chair again, his eyes going slowly over the small form held protectively against Davina's breast.

'My son, or your grandson, Madre?' he asked sardonically. 'Tell me. If I were still man enough to father children, if Sebastian could provide you with grandsons, would you still want *that*?'

The use of the derisive word, the look he gave them, all combined to arouse within Davina the anger the sight of him, stricken, had tempered. Quivering with the pent-up force of it, she advanced on the wheelchair, her eyes blazing almost as darkly as his, unaware of the arresting picture her erect carriage and pale face made.

'*That*, as you call him, just happens to be your son,' she told him, barely able to form the words coherently. 'The son you've denied from the moment of his birth, but he is your son, Ruy, and he will live here as is his birthright . . .'

'How you have changed your tune,' he sneered bitterly. 'When I married you, you told me that you wished I were a poor man; that we could live an "ordinary" life. What went wrong, Davina? Or is it just that with age has come the realisation that you will not be young for ever, that there will come a time when men cease to desire your body; when you will have nothing but the dead ashes of too many burnt out love affairs . . . My son! How can I be sure of that?'

The sharp crack of her palm against his lean cheek split the silence. Behind her Davina heard someone gasp, and she felt faintly sick herself as she stared at the dull red patch against the tanned skin. What had prompted her to behave so outrageously? In her arms Jamie stirred again and whispered, opening his eyes properly for the first time to stare at the man who had fathered him. How could Ruy so coldly deny his own flesh and blood? she asked herself. It was obvious that Jamie was his child . . .

'I apologise for striking you,' she said shakily, 'but you did provoke me. Did you think I would have come here for one moment had Jamie not been your child?'

'I know only that you disappeared out of my life, only to reappear now, at the command of my mother. I am not a fool, Davina, no matter what I might have appeared in the past. It must have been a tempting prospect; a useless cripple of a husband whose presence need not disturb you, and the rest of your life spent in luxury waiting for your child to step into his shoes.'

'Stop! That is enough, Ruy,' his mother commanded. 'If you must have the truth, I allowed Davina to think that *you* had written to her.' She shrugged when he stared frowningly at her. 'Enough of this foolish pride. Jamie is the only son you are likely to have, the only son this house is likely to have. It is only right and fitting that he is brought up here where his place will one day be . . .'

It was at that moment that Jamie decided it was time he took a hand in the proceedings himself. Struggling against Davina's guarding arms, he demanded to be put down on the floor. When she did as he requested he toddled solemnly over to the wheelchair, while Davina, her heart in her mouth, darted forward to hold him back. It was only the pressure of her mother-in-law's fingers biting into her wrist that prevented her from wrenching Jamie away, her grasp restricting her for long enough for Jamie to reach his goal. Once there he stared up at his father, his eyes, so like Davina's, staring perplexedly at this man who looked back at him with such cool haughtiness.

'Is he my daddy?'

The question was addressed by Davina, over his shoulder, the shrill, piping treble baby voice filling the tense silence.

Davina tried to speak and could not. She had a photograph of Ruy at home which she had shown to Jamie, and although she doubted that he could have recognised the man pictured there, she was not going to lie to her son merely to spare the feelings of the father who denied him.

She cleared her throat, but her voice was still husky as she answered his question, going down on her knees to draw him back from Ruy, as though she feared that he might harm the child.

'Then why doesn't he talk to me?' Jamie demanded, turning towards her. 'Doesn't he like me?'

Such an innocent question! It brought a lump to Davina's throat and moisture to her eyes. This was a moment she had faced over and over again in all her worst nightmares, trying to explain to Jamie why his father had rejected them, but she had never, even in the very worst of them, guessed that she would be called upon to do so in Ruy's presence.

It was the Condesa who came to her rescue, her voice for once almost gentle as she placed her hand on Jamie's shoulder and smiled down at him.

'Of course he likes you, *pequeño*. Is that not so, Ruy?'

'What man can deny his own flesh and blood?' Ruy drawled sardonically, and Davina wondered if she was alone in remembering the accusation he had just hurled at her about Jamie's parentage. She had come to Spain reluctantly, and only for Jamie's sake, and if anyone had told her that if Ruy had repudiated them that she would insist on remaining she would have denied it most emphatically. It was not in her nature to be mercenary or grasping, wealth and position mattered little in her book when balanced against love and happiness, but something in Ruy's cold condemnation and lack of feeling for both of them had aroused all her fiercest maternal instincts; and for the sake of her child she was prepared to suffer indignities she would never have tolerated merely for her own gain. Jamie was Ruy's son, he had every right to be here at the Palacio, but one thing was going to be made quite clear to both Ruy and his family.

'Jamie is your child, Ruy,' she told him calmly. 'Oh, I know why you would prefer not to believe it. I'm surprised you haven't already had our marriage set aside. Had you done so and married Carmelita, she might have had a son of your own to displace Jamie, and then none of this would have been necessary.'

His harsh laughter jarred, shocking her into immobility. 'Nothing is quite that easy. Jamie would still have been my heir, whether he is my child or not, simply because he bears my name . . .'

'And knowing that Carmelita refused to marry you?'

She didn't know what prompted her to goad him like that; perhaps it was the nagging ache deep down inside her, a wound which refused to heal; the memory of how she had felt when she first discovered that Ruy did not love her and was merely using her instead to be revenged upon the woman whom he did love.

'Carmelita had no place in her life for a platonic relationship with a man,' he told her cruelly, 'and since I can no longer give her what she desires, she has found it elsewhere.'

'Carmelita has recently married and gone back to Argentina, with her new husband,' Sebastian interrupted, and as he said the words, Davina felt the full picture falling into place. Ruy's mother had always wanted him to marry Carmelita, but now, knowing that her plans must come to nothing, she had decided to fall back on what was left to her . . . Jamie. Only he would never be allowed to become cold and uncaring like his father, Davina told herself. He would not be brought up to think himself lord of all that he surveyed, to walk roughshod over anything and anyone who stood in his way, to ruthlessly and remorselessly crush underfoot the dreams and hopes of others . . . as Ruy had crushed hers.

'It has been a long day, and Jamie is tired,' she told her mother-in-law. 'If someone could show us to our rooms . . .'

'Motherhood has taught you courage, little white dove,' Ruy mocked. 'So cool and brave. I wonder how deep it is, that cool façade . . .'

'Just as deep as it needs to be to protect my son,' Davina told him with a calm she was far from feeling. How long could she endure the sort of mental and verbal torment he was handing out and not crack under it? Hard on the heels of the thought came the comforting knowledge that she was unlikely to see much of him. He was, after all, hardly likely to seek her out . . .

'So you intend to stay?' The hooded eyes watching her were unreadable, but guessing that he had hoped to frighten her into running away, for a second time, Davina lifted her chin proudly to stare back at him. 'For Jamie's sake—yes. Personally I wouldn't touch so much as a peseta of your money, Ruy, but Jamie is your son and . . .'

'And you have no objection to touching what will one day be his?' her husband mocked savagely.

At her side Davina's hands turned into minute angry fists. That hadn't been what she had been going to say at all. She had been about to explain to him that Jamie had been ill, that he needed building up, despite his robust appearance, and that for her child's sake she was willing to endure the torment and insult of knowing herself unwanted in this house.

'Which rooms . . .' she began, ignoring Ruy and turning to his mother, but Ruy forestalled her, his face cruel and malevolent as he too turned towards the older woman, anticipating Davina's question. 'Yes, Madre, which rooms have you given my delightful wife and child? The bridal suite, which we occupied before?' He shook his head and the sneer was clearly visible now. 'I think not. This wheelchair might be able to perform miracles, as Dr Gonzales tells me, but it still cannot climb stairs.'

Davina wasn't the only one to gasp. Even the Condesa seemed to go a little paler, her mouth nearly as grim as her son's as she addressed him.

'What nonsense is this, Ruy? Jamie and Davina will have a suite of rooms to themselves.'

'They will share mine,' Ruy corrected softly. 'I will not have the servants gossiping about my wife who leaves me and then returns only when I can no longer act the part of her husband. Well?' he demanded, turning to Davina. 'Have you nothing to say, no protests to make? Are you not going to tell me that you will return to England rather than suffer the indignity of sharing a room—a bed—with a crippled wreck?'

Davina knew then what he was trying to do—that he was attempting to frighten her into leaving, and how close he had come to succeeding. The mere thought of sharing a room with him, of suffering the intimacies such proximity would bring, had started her stomach churning protestingly. He might not be able to act the part of a husband, as he put it, but he was still a man—the man she had loved, and although her love had died her memories had not.

'You won't drive me away, Ruy,' she told him quietly. 'No matter what you do, I intend to stay, for Jamie's sake.'

A servant had to be summoned and instructed to prepare a room for Jamie. Davina could feel the girl watching her as Ruy spoke to her, and although she could not quite catch what was being said, her skin prickled warningly. When she had gone Sebastian and Rosita excused themselves, and as Rosita hurried past her, Davina thought she glimpsed compassionate pity in the other girl's eyes.

'My poor timid sister-in-law,' Ruy mocked, correctly interpreting Rosita's look. 'She sincerely pities you, but you have nothing to fear—unless it is the acid tongue of a man who has drunk ambrosia only to find it turning to acid gall on his lips.'

'Acid burns,' Davina reminded him coolly. Her heart was thumping with heavy fear, and she longed to retract her statement that she intended to stay. Jamie, who had returned to her side, clutching at her for support, suddenly abandoned her to walk across to Ruy for a second time, eyeing him uncertainly.

'I have a pushchair too,' he told Ruy conversationally, while Davina listened with her heart in her mouth. 'Mummy pushes me in it when I get tired. Who pushes you?'

'I can push myself, 'Ruy told him curtly, but nevertheless, and much to her surprise, Davina saw him demonstrate to Jamie exactly how he could manoeuvre the chair. Something in her mother-in-law's stance caught her attention, and as she glanced across at her the other woman looked away, but not before Davina had seen the sheen of tears in her eyes.

How would she feel if that was her child confined to that chair? The sudden clenching fear of her heart gave her the answer, and for the first time she began to feel pity for the older woman. It was a dangerous thing she had done, summoning them here, and one which could alienate her completely from Ruy. She glanced across at him, her breath constricting in her throat as she saw

the two dark heads so close together. Ruy had lifted
Jamie on to his lap and the little boy was solemnly
examining the controls of the chair.

'He is Ruy's mirror image,' the Condesa said quietly.
All at once she looked very old, and Davina had to
force herself to remember how coldly this woman had
received her in this very room when Ruy had brought
her here as his new bride. The trouble was that she
had not been prepared for the hostility that greeted
her. But then she had not been prepared for anything,
least of all falling in love with Ruy. It had all happened
so quickly—too quickly, she thought soberly. She had
fallen in love with Ruy without knowing him. He had
married her for . . . For what? Revenge? For punishment? She shuddered suddenly, reflecting on the
harshness of a nature which could enable a man to turn
his back on the woman he loved and put another in
her place, merely as a means of punishment for some
small peccadillo. And yet the first time she met him
she had thought him the kindest man on earth—and
the most handsome.

It had been in Cordoba. She had gone on holiday
with friends—or more properly acquaintances—girls
she knew from her work at the large insurance offices
in London. Their main interest in Spain lay on its
beaches; flirting with the dark-eyed Spanish boys who
gave full rein to their ardent natures in the presence of
these Northern girls with their cool looks and warm
natures, so different from those of the girls of their own
country whose chastity was carefully protected until
marriage gave their husbands the right to initiate them
into the ways of love. Davina had felt differently. She
had come to Spain to explore its history—a history
which had fascinated her since her early teens, when

she had fallen in love with the mystery of a land ruled for centuries by the aristocratic, learned Moors, who had bequeathed to it not only their works of art, but also their colouring and fire.

She had been half way to falling in love with Ruy even before she met him, she acknowledged wryly, for her head had been stuffed with foolish dreams of handsome Moorish warriors astride Arab horses, flowing white robes cloaking lean bronzed limbs, glittering eyes softening only for the women they loved. A sigh trembled past her lips. That was how Ruy had first appeared to her—a heroic figure who seemed to spring suddenly out of nowhere, rescuing her from the gang of teenage boys who had been harassing her as she left the Mosque. His curt words had cut through them like a whiplash, dispersing them to the four winds, and her trembling gratitude at his timely intervention had changed to worshipful adoration when he had insisted on sweeping her off to a small café to drink coffee and tell him what she had been doing in Spain. He, it appeared, was in Cordoba on business. His family owned a hacienda where they bred bulls for the bullfight, and it was in connection with the annual *corrida*—the running of young untried bulls through the streets—that he was in Cordoba.

Davina had listened fascinated, held in thrall to the magnetism of the man; to the sheer pleasure of hearing him speak, his English perfect and yet still possessing something of the liquid gold of his own language.

She had agreed almost at once when he invited her to accompany him to watch the gypsies dancing the flamenco—not, as she discovered, the polished empty performance put on for the tourists, but the real thing; as different from the other as tepid water to champagne.

They had left before the climax; before the black-browed gypsy claimed his partner in the culmination of a dance so sexually explicit that merely watching it had brought the blood surging to her veins, her expression unknowingly betraying as she watched the dancers, and the man seated opposite her watched her. He had not lived his twenty-nine years without learning something of women, and what he saw in Davina's face told him, more surely than any words, the extent of her untutored innocence.

Davina hadn't known it, but it was that knowledge which had sealed her fate—as she later discovered.

When Ruy had proposed to her she had been robbed of words, dizzied and humbled by the sheer gratitude of knowing that the love she had come to feel for him in the short week they had been together was returned. She had had no knowledge when she accepted him that he was merely using her as a tool to torture the woman he really loved—the fiery Spanish beauty who could give him so much more than she herself could offer.

They had been married quietly—a church ceremony in keeping with Ruy's religion—and that had been the first time she realised that her husband possessed a title—that she had a title. It shouldn't have surprised her. He had about him an ingrained arrogance which should have warned her that here was no ordinary mortal. He had been a little amused by her stammered concern that she might not be able to match up to his expectations, that nothing in her life had prepared her for the role of Condesa; wife of a Spanish grandee. It was only when his amusement gave birth to bored impatience that Davina learned fear of her new husband, but this had been swiftly banished by the brief, almost tormenting caress of his lips against hers.

Prior to their marriage he had made no attempt to seduce her, and in her innocence she had mistaken this lack of desire for her as respect. She had often wondered, since her return to England, if she had not gone to him that first night after their arrival at the Palacio, had not let him see that she wanted him . . . and if he had not been in such a blazing rage of anger against his mother, whether he would not have made love to her; whether in fact it had been his intention to have their marriage annulled when Carmelita had been suitably brought to heel. But above all else Ruy was a man of honour. Once he had in actual fact made her his wife there was no going back—for either of them. Until she had conceived his son, and learned exactly why he had married her. With that knowledge how could she have remained? She might have suspected that all was not well between them, but until she was brought face to face with the truth she had been able to delude herself. When that was no longer possible she had escaped to London, taking Jamie with her, and leaving her mother-in-law to convey to her son the good news that he was now free . . .

Free . . . Her eyes were drawn irresistibly to the man in the wheelchair and for a brief moment pity over-whelmed her bitterness. Ruy would never be free again. Ruy, whose superb, physical, *male* body had taught her the full meaning of womanhood, never to make love, ride, swim or dance again.

'Look at her!' His words cut through her thoughts. 'She cries. For what, my lovely wife? For having to share my bed and being perhaps tormented by all that we once knew together, or have other men, other lovers, obliterated the memory of the pleasure I taught you?'

'Ruy!'

His mouth twisted bitterly at the warning tone in his mother's voice. 'What is it, Madre?' he demanded savagely. 'Am I to be denied the pleasure of speaking about love as well as that of experiencing it, or does it offend you that a man in my condition should have such thoughts? You who brought me the news that the woman I loved had left me . . .'

So the Condesa had been the one to tell Ruy that Carmelita was leaving him . . . Davina repressed a small shudder. She couldn't understand how the other girl could have done it. Had she been in her shoes, she thought with a fierce stab of pain, had she been the recipient of Ruy's love, nothing would have kept her from his side. He might be physically restricted, but he was still the same man; still very much a man! Her wayward thoughts shocked her, widening her eyes as purple as the hearts of pansies with mingled pain and disbelief. She was over Ruy. She had put the past behind her. All the love she had now was focused on Jamie. As though to reinforce the thought she reached out for the child, and her hair brushed Ruy's chin as she did so.

His withdrawal was immediate and unfeigned, and as she lifted Jamie from his lap, Davina was dismayed to discover that she was trembling. What was it about this man that had the power to affect her like this even now—so much so that his rejection of her was like the stabbing of a thousand knives?

Grateful that Jamie gave her an excuse to look away from the contempt she felt sure must be in his eyes, she busied herself with the little boy, listening to his informative chatter.

A manservant appeared, silent-footed and grave-faced, and positioned himself behind Ruy's chair.

'This is Rodriguez, my manservant,' he told Davina sardonically. 'The third member of our new *ménage à trois*. You will have to grow accustomed to him, since he performs for me all those tasks I can no longer perform for myself. Unless of course you wish to take them over for yourself ... as a penance perhaps ... and a fitting one. You took pleasure from my body when it was physically perfect, Davina, so perhaps it is only just that you should endure its deformity now.'

'Ruy!'

Davina thought her mother-in-law's protest was on account of the indelicacy of her son's conversation, but she ought to have known better, Davina decided, when she continued angrily, 'The doctor has told you, the paralysis need not be permanent. Much can be done ...'

'To make me walk like an animal, used to moving on all fours—yes, I know.' Ruy dismissed the notion impatiently, disgust curling the corners of his mouth. 'Thank you, Madre, but no. You have interfered enough in my life as it is.' His glance embraced both Davina and the child held in her arms. 'Rodriguez, you will take me to my room. Davina.'

When her mutely imploring glance at her mother-in-law went unheeded Davina followed the manservant reluctantly down the long passage leading off the hall, to a suite of rooms she dimly remembered as being what Ruy had once described as a 'bachelor suite'. It had been the custom for young male members of the family to live apart from their sisters and mothers after a certain age, he had told her. The custom had originated from the days when his Moorish ancestors had been jealous of their wives, and any male eyes which might look upon them.

From what she could remember the suite was quite large, built around its own pàtio, and as Rodriguez opened the double panelled doors leading into the *sala* Davina heard the sound of fountains playing outside and knew that she had not been mistaken.

In contrast to the rest of the house the room was furnished almost simply, with clean, uncluttered furniture that combined the best of antique and modern. The dark blue azulejo tiles were covered with a Persian carpet—a rich mingling of blues and scarlets, touched here and there with gold and pricelessly expensive. On a marble coffee table placed strategically next to a cream hide chesterfield were some magazines, and again Davina felt her heart twist with pity that Ruy was reduced to finding his pleasure in such a passive way.

'You remember this part of the house?'

She refused to look at him. He had brought her to this *sala* after that dreadful scene with his mother, when the older woman had accused her of trapping him into marriage, of forcing him to make an honest woman of her. It was in here that he had dried her tears before leading her out on to the patio, where she had flung herself despairingly into his arms and they had walked into the orange grove and . . .

'I'm hungry!' Jamie eyed her crossly. 'Mummy, I'm hungry!'

'You hear that, Rodriguez?' Ruy demanded with an upward lift of his eyebrows. 'My son is hungry. He is not yet used to our way of life.'

A smile glimmered across the other man's sombre features.

'Maria shall make you a paella, and you shall have oranges picked fresh from the trees,' Ruy promised him. 'Only be patient for a little while.'

Davina was a little surprised at Jamie's immediate response to the authority in his father's voice. Perhaps it was true that all boys needed the firmness of a father's hand. But would Ruy let his obvious bitterness against her spill out to sour his relationship with his son? Had she known that the invitation to come to Spain was not from him she knew she would never have ventured here to the Palacio, and yet having done so, she was strangely reluctant to return again to England.

The courtyard outside was all in darkness, but the patio doors had been left open to allow the scents of the night to drift in—the spicy, sharp smell of the oranges, a constant reminder of that night when Jamie had been conceived; the sweetness of night-scented stocks, those timid, almost insipid flowers that only revealed their true beauty during the hours of darkness when their perfume filled the night air.

If she remembered rightly, beyond the patio was a swimming pool. She had swum in it once with Ruy. She pushed the thought aside, unwilling to remember the warmth of Ruy's arms around her as he pulled her down beneath the silken water, only releasing her when her lips had been subjected to a masterful, demanding kiss. Then she had thought that he loved her. She had not known about Carmelita.

The *sala* connected with a smaller room which had been turned into a tiny kitchen, presumably so that Ruy could be completely independent of the rest of the household if he wished, and Davina sensed intuitively that there must be many times when his pride could no longer bear the lash of enduring the silent pity of the rest of his family; when he must prefer to be hidden from the world to suffer alone. And yet he had insisted that she and Jamie were to share his suite, to share his torment . . .

Beyond the kitchen was a room which had been converted into a bedroom, opulently rich in its furnishings, but it was the huge double bed which drew Davina's eyes, fear hidden in their amethyst depths as she stared at it.

'Where's my bed?' Jamie demanded suddenly, breaking the silence. 'And where's my mummy's bed?'

'Your mummy's bed is here,' Ruy said silkily, turning aside to murmur something to Rodriguez, who disappeared in soft-footed silence through a door at the far end of the room.

'Through that door is the bathroom,' Ruy told Davina when he had gone, 'and beyond that a dressing room. Jamie shall sleep there for the time being.'

'And I shall sleep with him,' Davina said bravely. At home she had only a very small flat, and Jamie's small bed was in the same room as hers. It would frighten the small boy to find himself sleeping alone, but when she attempted to explain this to Ruy he cut across her explanation, his voice harsh as he said cruelly, 'You will sleep here in this room in my bed, Davina, otherwise Jamie will be banished to another part of the house. Do you understand me?'

'Why?'

His eyes searched her face, and for the first time she saw the true extent of his bitterness.

'Why? Because you are my wife,' he said softly. 'Because I will not endure the pitying glances of my servants and my family when it becomes known that my wife has returned to me only because she knows she will no longer be expected to undergo the degradation of sharing my bed. That was what you once called it, wasn't it?' he continued unmercifully. 'Degradation of the very worst sort? You don't even begin to know what it means, but you will learn, sharing this room with me, being forced to witness all the thousand and one indignities that my ... my disability forces upon me. In fact ...' his eyes roamed her set white face, 'I think you *should* take the place of Rodriguez.'

His fingers snaked out, grasping her wrist and making her gasp with pain, unable to believe that their hard, vibrant warmth belonged to a man who was no longer fully in control of his own body. 'It hurts? You should be grateful that you can feel pain,' he concluded grimly. '*Madre de Dios*, I wish I could!'

Davina swallowed a lump in her throat. Despite his desire to hurt and wound her, she could not prevent pity welling up inside her. Dear God, what torment he must be in, this man who had always taken for granted his male power. To find it cut off like this must surely be the worst blow fate could have dealt him. She knew she ought to feel some sense of satisfaction, some pleasure in knowing that he was now suffering as he had once caused her to suffer, but all she could feel was an overwhelming desire to reach out and brush the silky black hair off his forehead, to hold and comfort him as she might have done Jamie ... The thought stunned her, rooting her to the spot as she stared blindly around her, not seeing the elegant room with its rich furnishings, the carved bed, the Persian carpets, the antique furniture, the elegant graciousness of a house that had been inhabited by Ruy's family for generation after generation; children brought up in a tradition, children of whom her son was the latest.

The door opened suddenly, and Rodriguez appeared with her luggage. Without looking at Ruy Davina followed him through the bathroom with its sunken bath in jade green malachite, the taps in the same material, azulejo tiles adorning the floor.

Beyond it was a small plainly furnished room overlooking the courtyard, with a single bed and a carved chest of drawers. When they were alone Davina undressed Jamie, before taking him back to the bathroom to wash his hands and face before she put him to bed. He chattered continuously, and she answered his questions almost mechanically, her mind still in that other bedroom with the man whose child Jamie was.

As though on cue, the moment Jamie was installed in bed the door opened again, and this time a woman came in carrying a tray, steaming fragrantly.

Jamie was not a fussy eater, and he tucked into the paella with such obvious relish that Davina had to repress a small smile. Contrary to her expectations Jamie seemed to be adapting very well to his new surroundings—far better than she was likely to do herself.

Only when she was quite sure that he was asleep did she return to the other room, unable to repress her feeling of relief when she saw Sebastian in the room, talking to Ruy.

'Ruy, will you not reconsider?' Davina heard him saying in a low voice as she re-entered the room. 'Surely you wish to spare Davina the . . .'

'The sight of my crippled limbs?' Ruy said harshly. 'Why? Am I spared them? Am I spared anything? No, it will do no good to plead for compassion for my wife, Sebastian,' he added cruelly. 'Or is it guilt that brings you to this room, little brother? After all, had you provided Madre with her grandson, there would be no need for Davina to be here, would there?'

A small sound must have betrayed Davina's presence, for both men turned at the same time.

'Ah, there you are,' Ruy drawled in a false parody of tenderness. 'Just in time to help me change for dinner.'

'I don't want any dinner,' Davina began, but her protest was overruled by Sebastian's angry protest.

'You cannot do this!' he told Ruy. 'You cannot mean to subject your wife to such indignity . . . Have you no compassion, Ruy? How is Jamie?' he asked Davina, turning to her. 'Has he settled down all right?'

'Better than I expected,' Davina told him. There was guilt and embarrassment in his eyes, and she thought she knew now why he had been so offhand with her at the airport. It was obvious that his mother had told him to say nothing of Ruy's condition to her, and now he felt guilty about the way his brother was treating her.

'Rosita had better be careful,' Ruy commented sardonically when Sebastian had gone. 'My little brother's concern for you is most touching. I trust you have something better than that to wear for dinner,' he added, giving her slender figure a disparaging glance. 'You will not have forgotten that we observe the formalities here at the Palacio.'

She hadn't. Since Jamie's birth and her flight to England there hadn't been any money for luxuries like evening dresses, but she still had the clothes Ruy had insisted on buying for her after their marriage—when he had realised that he was irrevocably tied to her, and had tried to make the best of their mesalliance. Her mouth twisted a little bitterly and for the first time she realised that she had been handed a weapon which she could use to gain reparation in full for all the hurt Ruy had caused her, if she chose to use it. She was to take the place of his manservant, or so he had commanded, and if she chose, she could make the performance of those small intimate tasks which would be required of her as humiliatingly agonising for Ruy as he had once made her life for her!

'You will go and prepare yourself for dinner,' Ruy commanded her curtly, frowning when she made no attempt to move.

'Don't you want me to help you first?'

Something in the soft tone of her voice must have made him suspicious, because he frowned darkly, manoeuvring his chair past her. 'Not tonight,' he said abruptly. 'I am hungry, and I don't propose to wait all evening for you to perform the tasks Rodriguez can perform in half the time.' He glanced at his watch, pushing back the cuff of his shirt, and Davina felt her stomach constrict painfully at the sight of his lean, sinewy wrist, and the dark hairs curling against the gold mesh of his watch-strap. All too vividly she could remember how that hand had so arrogantly caressed her yielding flesh, had turned her from girl to woman and taught her pleasure . . .

CHAPTER THREE

SHE had endured many formal dinners during her days at the Palacio, but none which had tautened her muscles to breaking point as this one was doing, Davina reflected, as the long meal seemed to drag on interminably.

On the table her glass of sherry still stood barely touched. It was Silvadores sherry, matured in their own *bodega* near Cadiz; the very best *fino*, dry and clean to the palate. The first time she had tasted it Davina had found it too dry, but habit had accustomed her taste-buds; all those long, lazy afternoons whose end had been signalled by the serving of sherry and tapas on the patio. She clamped down on the thought. On too many thoughts.

'You are not hungry?'

It was Rosita who whispered the words understandingly, but Ruy who answered them for her, even though they were separated by the length of the polished table, gleaming with silver and crystal. The Silvadores had no need to parade their wealth ostentatiously, and Davina knew that the fine china plates and silver cutlery they were using were nothing compared with the exquisite Sèvres and Meissen china locked away with the gold plate which was a legacy from the Conde who had sailed to the Americas. The family's wealth derived from many sources—from the sherry business, from land they owned all over Spain, from the young bulls raised on the *estancia*; from busi-

ness ventures involving the development of exclusive
holiday resorts—but it was here in this ancient
Moorish castle that they had set their deepest roots.
And Ruy was the sole ruler of this empire. How had
his accident occurred? By what means had he been
robbed of his independence? Davina glanced down the
length of the table. Seeing him seated no one could
guess that the powerful muscles moving smoothly beneath his dinner jacket were all that remained of his
old physical perfection.

As the meal dragged on images as sharp and crystal
clear as the day they were formed imposed themselves
relentlessly on her mind; Ruy swimming in the pool;
Ruy riding at the *estancia*, training the young bulls
destined for the arena; Ruy dancing . . . making love
. . . She shuddered deeply and wrenched her thoughts
back to the present, trying to tell herself that it was
divine justice that Ruy, who had cruelly and callously
used her to get back at the woman he really loved,
should now be deserted by that woman. Why had
Carmelita done it? Davina wondered. She had been a
bride of a matter of weeks when the sultry Spanish
woman had sought her out at this very house, reinforc-
ing what Davina had already heard from her mother-
in-law—that Ruy loved her; that there had been an
understanding between them for many years; that they
were on the point of announcing their betrothal when
they had quarrelled, and Ruy in a fit of pique because
she, Carmelita, did not choose to run to his bidding
like the milk and water English miss he had married
had chosen a bride as different from the seductive
Spaniard with her night-dark hair and carmine lips as
it would have been possible to find. She would get him
back, Carmelita had told her. A milksop like her could

never hold a man like Ruy, whose lovemaking demanded from his partner a deep-seated understanding of the complexities that went into the making of a man whose blood combined the fiery fanaticism of early Christianity with thousands of years of Moorish appreciation of the sensual arts—a woman such as Carmelita herself.

And yet now Carmelita had abandoned him. Because he was no longer the man he had once been; no longer capable of outriding the wind, of making love until dawn tinted the sky, or because her pride would not allow any child she bore him to come second to the son his English wife had given him? Under the polite mask of Spanish courtesy lay deep wells of passion that were a legacy of their Moorish ancestors, as Davina already knew. Who could say what had prompted Carmelita to desert Ruy and make her life with another?

At last the meal drew to a close, but instead of feeling relieved Davina felt her nerves tighten still further, the implacable determination in Ruy's eyes like the fiendish threat of a torturer ready to turn the screws that final notch which separated excruciating pain from oblivion by the mere hair's breadth.

All through the meal she had answered her mother-in-law's questions about Jamie's upbringing as politely as she could. Once she might have been intimidated by this woman whose ancestors had numbered kings and queens among their intimates, but where Jamie was concerned she would allow nothing to stand in the way of what she considered right for her child, and this she had been making coolly and firmly clear to Ruy's mother throughout the meal.

By the time she realised she was carrying Jamie she

had been too numbed by pain to care, for by then she
had known exactly why Ruy had married her, and why
too he spent so many hours away from the Palacio—
away from her bed. The baby she had been carrying
had been incidental to her pain, but after his birth she
had been overwhelmed by such love for Jamie that that
pain had started to recede, if only minutely. As she
held him to her breast and felt him suckle strongly she
had known that whatever the cost to herself Jamie
would not be brought up in a house where his mother
was despised. And her mother-in-law had aided her in
her flight. She had been the one who had brought those
damning photographs of Ruy and Carmelita together
at the *estancia*, while she, his wife, bore his child alone.
She had left the hospital one cold, grey winter afternoon, taking a plane for London, not knowing what
path her life would take, but only knowing that she
must get away from Spain and Ruy before her love for
him destroyed her completely.

She had been lucky—very lucky, she acknowledged
wryly. The chance entering of a competition in a
women's magazine had led to a contract for illustrations for a magazine serial and from there to her present work on children's books. She was not rich, but
she had enough to buy a small flat in a Pembrokeshire
village; enough to keep Jamie and herself in modest
comfort, but not enough to give the little boy the warm
winters he needed until his strength was built up.

After dinner while Rodriguez served coffee in the
sala Sebastian came and sat beside her.

'You must try to forgive Ruy,' he told her awkwardly
in a low voice while his brother was speaking to the
manservant. 'He has changed since his accident.' He
shrugged explicitly. 'Who would not, especially a man

like Ruy who was always so . . .'

'Male?' Davina supplied wryly, watching the blood surge faintly beneath Sebastian's olive skin. 'Oh yes, I can guess at the devils that torment him now, Sebastian, but what I can't understand is how your mother dared to conceal from him that she was sending for me.'

Sebastian shrugged again, this time avoiding her eyes completely. 'You have seen how Ruy reacted. Just as she knew that you would not come if you knew the truth, so she knew that Ruy would not allow you to be sent for. He has his pride . . .'

'And was deserted by the woman he loves,' Davina supplied.

Sebastian looked surprised and uncomfortable. 'That is so, but my brother is not the man to enforce his emotions on a woman who does not want them. You need have no fears on that score, Davina.'

'I haven't,' she told him dryly. 'I'm well aware that the only reason I'm tolerated here is because of Jamie; the son Ruy has always refused to acknowledge . . . the son who even now he tries to pretend might not be his . . .'

The telephone rang and Sebastian excused himself hurriedly, leaving her alone. Stifling a yawn, she closed her eyes, meaning only to rest them for a few minutes.

Whether it was the faint hiss of the wheelchair, or some sixth sense alerting her to another's presence that woke her, Davina did not know. When she opened her eyes the *sala* was in darkness apart from one solitary lamp casting a pool of soft rose light over the ancient Persian carpet.

'So, you are awake. I seem to remember that you had difficulty before adjusting to our hours.'

'You should have woken me before.' A glance at her wristwatch confirmed that it was late—nearly two in the morning. They were the only occupants of the room, and her sense of vulnerability increased as she realised that Ruy had watched her as she slept, observed her in her most unguarded moments. No, not her most unguarded, she acknowledged seconds later; those had been when they made love. She shivered involuntarily, the light shining whitely on Ruy's teeth as he bared them mockingly.

'Why do you shake so, *querida*?' he asked dulcetly. 'Can it be that you are afraid of me? A man who cannot move without the assistance of this chair? You fear the caged tiger, where you would not fear the free?'

It was on the tip of her tongue to point out that caged tigers could be unmercifully lethal, driven to scar and wound by the very virtue of their imprisonment, and so it was with Ruy himself. In him she sensed all the dammed-up power and bitterness of a man for whom life has lost its sharp sweetness and turned to aloes on his tongue.

'What is it you fear most, my little wife?' He was close enough for her to smell the sherry on his breath and to remember with contracting stomach muscles the taste of his lips on hers. 'That I shall exact payment for your desertion of me; for depriving me of my son?'

'You could have come after us,' Davina reminded him levelly. 'If you'd really wanted us. . . .'

He made a harsh, guttural sound in his throat, his eyes darkening to anger. 'Is that what you wanted in a husband, Davina, a man who would prove himself to you over and over again? And the man you left me for? The Englishman who meant more to you than your marriage vows—what happened to him, or did he no longer want you when you stopped calling yourself the Condesa de Silvadores?'

Davina had never been able to think of the title in connection with herself, but she was too bewildered by what Ruy had said to pay too much attention to his reminder that she had stopped using his name when she left his house. There had been no man in her life since the day she met Ruy, apart from his son, and it infuriated her to think that he dared to berate her about some imagined lover when he . . .

'There was no one!' she started to protest angrily, but Ruy's expression said that he did not believe her.

'No?' he sneered. 'You are lying to me, *querida*. You were seen with him in Seville. And it is known that you left Spain with him, taking my child with you.'

From the past Davina conjured up the memory of a bearded, fair-haired fellow-Briton she had met in Seville. He had been an artist, and with this common bond between them they had started talking. Davina dimly remembered that her mother-in-law had found them chatting enthusiastically to one another in a small pavement café, and she, innocent that she was, had assumed the older woman's contempt sprang from discovering her drinking coffee in such a shabby little place, but now, with the benefit of hindsight, she realised that the Condesa must have thought she was having an affair, perhaps as a means of getting back at Ruy. So now she knew why Ruy had been so reluctant to believe that Jamie was his—and she hadn't helped. Although she had known of her pregnancy she had said nothing for several months, trapped in the bitterness of knowing herself unloved and keeping the knowledge of Jamie's conception to herself as though she could use it as a talisman to ward off the threat of Carmelita.

'At least you now acknowledge that Jamie is your child,' was all she said. No matter what else might lie unspoken about between them, she was not going to have any aspersions or doubts cast on Jamie's parentage.

'So everyone tells me,' Ruy agreed bitterly. 'He must have been conceived during our honeymoon, before . . .'

'Before I discovered the real reason why you married me?' Davina demanded proudly. Once she had known about Carmelita she had steadfastly refused to share Ruy's bed, even though by doing so she was causing herself the utmost pain. There hadn't been a single night when she had not lain awake until the early hours remembering how it had felt to drift off to sleep in Ruy's arms, feeling the strong, reassuring thud of his heart against her ear, knowing herself held secure against all the dangers the world had to offer, but she had not been safe; Ruy's arms were not a haven, and he had never intended them to be. He had taken her because he felt sorry for her; because she had made her desire for him so plain that he could not in all compassion do anything else. Even now it made her writhe in self-torment to remember their 'honeymoon'. Until the marriage ceremony was over she had known nothing about the Palacio, or Ruy's family. He was taking her to his home, was all he had told her in answer to her excited questions; to the house built in the protective lee of the Sierras where Silvadores brides had come since the Moors first settled this part of Spain.

She had been excited and tremulous; excited because this handsome, sophisticated man had chosen her as his bride, and tremulous because she was stepping out of one world and into another. She knew next to nothing about men, having experienced only the chaste, fumbled kisses of the boys she had known at home. Her parents were both dead and she had been brought up by a grandmother who adhered to the moral code of her own generation, and thus Davina had not had the same licence permitted to her school friends. She remembered that Ruy had laughed when she tried to explain that he would not find her experienced in the ways of love, as were her contemporaries. Did she think he was blind? he had mocked tenderly. Did she honestly think he could not recognise an unblemished bud, still unopened? and she had been content to leave it there, not knowing that beneath the words lay the bitter thread of self-mockery, for the woman he should have married in her place was of his culture and sophistication, and knew all the ways there were of pleasuring a man, while she . . .

She grimaced slightly to herself. Was she so very different now? She might have borne a child, but she was no more experienced now than she had been when she left Ruy. All her body knew of pleasure had been imparted to it by him; and while he had not loved her he had been a courteous teacher, leading her gently into the paths of sensuality.

She hadn't realised that Ruy had crossed the room until the scent of oranges filled the air and she realised that he had pushed open the patio doors and was sitting with his back to her staring out into the night.

As the delicate fragrance filled the room, her thoughts were dragged unwillingly to the past; to her arrival at the Palace of the Orange Trees, that first dreadful dinner when the Condesa had unleashed upon her unprotected head all her chagrin and fury at her son's choice of bride, and Ruy had found her prone upon the bed in the room she had been given—quite separate from his—crying as though her heart would break. She had been too engrossed in her own misery then to be aware of the undercurrents eddying strongly all about her; of Carmelita, whose dark passionate beauty had repelled her, like an overblown flower with the touch of decadence already upon it, or of why the Spanish girl had looked at her with such hatred in her eyes.

Ruy had dried her tears, had told her that all would seem better in the morning. Davina had begged him not to leave her alone, half hysterical at the thought of staying in her room, separated from the man who was now her husband, and she had been relieved when he suggested that they walk through the orange grove, to give her time to calm herself.

The evening had been mild, stars spangling the sky, the scent of the oranges drifting all around them. Ruy had taken her arm—more out of courtesy than desire, she now realised, and if she had not stumbled over a tussock of grass who knew what might have happened, but she had done, and Ruy had bent to catch her, causing them both to overbalance, and there beneath the orange trees she had looked at him with her heart in her eyes and mutely begged him to make her his wife in deed as well as thought.

He had seemed to draw back from her, but she, without shame, thinking that he returned her love and was thinking only of propriety, had flung her arms round his neck, pressing small agonised kisses to his throat, drinking in the taste of his warm male flesh. The outcome was inevitable. Ruy was a very male man after all, and even if she was not the woman he loved she was there in his arms, and very, very available. He had been tender with her and careful, she could not fault him on that, and it was only later that she realised had he loved her more he might have found it hard to be quite so temperate. Even so, despite his care, his possession had caused her to cry out, the soft sound silenced by his mouth, and later, when she had slept a little, he had made love to her again, and this time there had been no pain. They had returned to the house, the scent of his flesh mingling with the perfume of the oranges, the two inextricably linked in her mind for all time, so that since she had left the Palacio she had been unable to touch the fruit.

After that they had been given adjoining rooms, and no matter how late it was when Ruy retired Davina had padded through to his room, begging him mutely to take her in his arms and reassure her that he still loved her. Dear God, what a crass fool she had been! He had never loved her at all. He had felt pity for her, that was all.

She had discovered the truth while he was visiting the bodega in Cadiz. She had wanted to go with him, but he had told her he would not be gone long. He wasn't, but it was still long enough for her world to come toppling down over her ears when her mother-in-law and then Carmelita opened her eyes to the truth. When Ruy returned she had had her things moved to another bedroom. He had never questioned her about her decision and she had never told him. The first few nights had been sleepless, while she listened in vain for the sound of him coming to seek her out, but why should he, when he had Carmelita, who could offer him so much more than she ever could? Carmelita, in whose veins ran some of the proudest blood of Spain. Carmelita, who could match him skill for skill, passion for passion; Carmelita, whose vivid beauty paled her own to a violet next to a hybrid rose. It had been that week while Ruy was away that Davina had met Bob Wilson in Seville and had been seen with him by Ruy's mother; it had also been that week that she first suspected she was carrying Ruy's child.

'Do you intend to sit there all night? Is the thought of sharing a room with me so repellent that you would rather sleep upright in a chair? How you have changed!' Ruy mocked savagely. 'I can remember a time when you couldn't wait to share my bed—didn't wait, in fact.' He laughed without humour when he saw her white face illuminated in the pale glow of the single lamp. 'Do not look so afraid, *amada*, I can no longer walk with you through the orange groves of my home and give way to an emotion as eternal as man . . .'

Tormented by the images conjured by his careless words, Davina got to her feet. 'I'm surprised you can remember,' she said bitterly. 'After all, it was a long time ago and scarcely important.'

'You think not?' In the shadows his face seemed to harden, pain mingling with bitterness in the eyes that raked her from head to foot—a trick of the shadows, she imagined, for there was no reason why it should cause Ruy pain to think of their marriage, unless it was because of all that that simple ceremony had deprived him of. 'You think a man forgets the vows he makes, so easily. I am not like you, Davina. I cannot treat our marriage so lightly.'

There was a brooding quality to the words that made Davina wonder if this was why he had not taken steps to have their marriage set aside before. Marriage was something which was taken very seriously in Spain, but surely Ruy had thought of this before the ceremony that made them man and wife? But then he had never intended it to be more than just a ceremony, she reminded herself, suddenly overwhelmed by a terrible feeling of guilt. If it had not been for her, for her foolish belief that he loved her, he could have been free to marry Carmelita, to father children on the woman he loved, instead of which ... She turned towards him impulsively, the moonlight turning her hair to silver and her eyes to dark mysterious pools of darkest purple, her expression unconsciously pleading as she reached out to him.

'Ruy, I know ours isn't an ideal situation, but must we be enemies? For Jamie's sake can't we try to put aside our differences, to ...'

The explosive curse ripped from his throat froze her where she stood. When he turned to face her his face was white with held-in anger. 'You can say that so easily,' he said harshly, 'but then it would suit you, wouldn't it? A wife, but yet not a wife; secure in your position within this household and yet absolved from the duties that go with that position. Is that why you came back? Because you perceived how you could have the best of both worlds ... Because you knew you would not have to share my bed?'

'I knew nothing about your accident,' Davina told him, shocked that he could think her capable of such calculation and greed.

'So, what is it you are offering me? Your pity?' His face contorted savagely. 'Keep it, for I do not want it. You are here on my sufferance alone, and sufferance is the operative word, Davina. Be careful that I don't decide to exact penance for my suffering. Come, it is time we retired.'

She moved towards his chair, but he motioned to her to precede him towards his own suite, which she did, wishing her heart would not thump so painfully, and that she had not been foolish enough to allow Ruy to see her compassion for him. He was a bitter man, and bitter men sometimes delighted in inflicting pain on others purely to relieve their own anguish. But could whatever pain he chose to force her to endure now compare with the agony she had known when she realised she did not have his love?

She had half expected to find the manservant Rodriguez waiting for Ruy in his room, despite the latter's comments earlier in the evening, but when Ruy switched on the light and flooded the room with bright colour she saw that it was empty.

She was just about to step out of the room to check on Jamie when Ruy seized her wrist painfully tight. Whatever might have happened to his lower body the muscles of his arms and chest were as hard and firm as ever.

'Oh no, you don't escape so easily,' he mocked her softly. 'You elected to come back here of your own free will, my dear wife, and now you must start to perform those duties which fate has chosen to be yours.'

On the bed Davina saw a towelling robe which was obviously Ruy's, and one of the thin silk nightdresses she had brought with her from home.

'I wonder what was in the mind of the maid who laid out those things,' Ruy drawled, following her eyes to the bed. 'Was pity there for you, do you suppose, because you are condemned to share the bed of a man who is no man at all?'

'Stop it!' Davina's hands closed over her ears to blot out the harsh sound of Ruy's bitter laughter, but he reached for her wrists, dragging them downwards, so that she was forced to listen to his hatefully cold voice as he told her unmercifully, 'I have wished many times to blot out the truth, but God has not yet granted me the ability to do so. Who knows, perhaps tonight, with you in my bed, I might discover some panacea for the nightmares which haunt me. Help me to undress,' he commanded abruptly. 'It has been a long evening—longer perhaps than any other I have ever known.'

Davina glanced wildly towards the door and wetted her dry lips with the tip of her tongue. 'Surely Rodriguez——' she began uncertainly, but Ruy cut her off impatiently.

'Rodriguez is asleep in his own bed, would you have me wake him because of your selfish revulsion about seeing my body? What is it you fear the most? Looking upon my useless limbs, perhaps? Being forced to touch the dead skin and muscle?'

He sounded so cool, but beneath the controlled sarcasm of his words Davina could sense the dammed-up bitterness, and knew she could not tell him that what she feared was his loss of control if he found the strain of torturing both her and himself too much. Because to torture her was to torture himself, to reveal his innermost scars. Wanting to bring his torment to an end as much for himself as for her, she hurried to his side and began to unfasten the buttons of his shirt. It was a task she had performed countless thousands of times for Jamie and should have meant nothing to her at all, but the smooth brown flesh beneath her fingers was not a child's but a man's; the heart beating steadily that which had lulled her to sleep, the crisp mat of dark hairs on the lean chest an unbearable reminder of the strength and warmth of his body possessing her own.

'Come,' Ruy jeered softly, when she trembled, 'I can remember a time when you were swifter than this, although then too your fingers shook, but then you had something to anticipate, did you not? Then it was desire and not fear that shone from your stormcloud eyes.'

She had his shirt completely unfastened, the taut flesh of his chest rising and falling with the rhythm of his breathing. Perspiration beaded his upper lip and beneath her palms his flesh felt warm and moist. She tried to force herself not to remember how on other occasions she had touched her lips to his skin, drinking in the feel and taste of him, running her tongue along the hard bones of his shoulders, absorbing the scent and feel of him with senses blind to everything but him.

She was bending to remove his shoes when she heard the cry from the other room. Jamie! She straightened up, her eyes flying to the door, and Ruy's followed them.

'He must be something special, this child I have given you, for you to care so deeply about him. What is it, I wonder?'

'He hasn't been well.' The words came jerkily from between her lips, as she remembered exactly how ill Jamie had been. 'Please, I must go to him.' She rose to her feet in one lithe movement, hurrying to the door and opening it.

Jamie was clutching his battered teddybear, his eyes wide and frightened.

'Mummy, I wanted you and you wasn't there,' he reproached gently. 'I was frightened!'

'What of, darling?' Davina asked him, kneeling down to push the thick dark hair, so like his father's, out of his eyes. 'You're quite safe here. You've got Teddy to look after you, and Mummy will be sleeping in the next room.'

'I want it to be like it is at home,' Jamie protested. 'I want you to sleep in my room.'

Suppressing a sigh, Davina explained to him that this was not possible. His room was very small, she told him, and there was not enough room for another bed.

She could share his, Jamie said reasonably, and when Davina told him that it wasn't big enough he said that his daddy could have this little room and then there would be enough room for Jamie and Mummy in Daddy's bed.

Sighing again, Davina reminded him that mummies and daddies slept in the same bed, just like in his story books, reflecting that while Jamie seemed to accept the presence of his father without too much curiosity this matter of the shared bedroom promised to be more difficult. The doctor had told her during Jamie's illness that it was unwise for her to have him in her room. 'Pretty girl like you—bound to marry again,' he had told her gruffly, 'and my lad here isn't going to take kindly to that if this state of affairs goes on much longer.'

Only when she was quite sure that Jamie was deeply asleep did Davina return to Ruy's room. It was in darkness and for a moment she thought that Ruy had come to his senses and decided to leave her and Jamie alone, but this thought was speedily despatched when her eyes grew accustomed to the darkness of the room and she saw the humped figure in the large double bed. The wheelchair was neatly folded beside the bed, and she frowned, wondering how Ruy had managed to finish undressing himself and get himself from the wheelchair into the bed—unless of course his disability was less severe than she had thought.

'Are are you coming to bed, or are you going to stand there all night like a nervous virgin?'

She had thought him asleep, and jumped as he rolled over on to his side, his eyes piercing the darkness as they searched for and found her.

She was in half a mind to demand a separate room, but her eye was caught by the wheelchair and a wave of pity overwhelmed her, softening her animosity towards him. Besides, she could hardly get one of the maids out of bed at this hour of the night, and if Jamie should wake again he would wonder where she had gone.

'In a moment,' she told him, surprised to discover how calm her voice was. 'First I want to have a bath.'

The bathroom was a sybaritic pleasure all on its own. The bath was wide and deep enough for two, set into the tiled floor, so that she had to step down into it. How did Ruy manage? she wondered as she sprinkled rose-scented bath crystals on the water and lay back, luxuriating in its perfumed warmth.

Ten minutes later, feeling relaxed and refreshed, she stepped out of the jade green tub and reached for the towel she had left in readiness. A mirrored wall threw her reflection back to her, emphasising her pale slenderness; the narrow waist and hips and the curved fullness of her breasts with their rose pink nipples. Since Jamie's birth her figure had become more voluptuous and it seemed to her disturbed gaze that her breasts seemed to swell and tauten, anticipating the touch of a lover. Dragging her eyes from the mirror, she wrapped herself quickly in a towel, rubbing herself dry briskly before slipping on her nightgown. Only when the slip of soft pink silk concealed her body did she turn back to the mirror and smooth moisturiser into her skin.

In the bedroom she found her hairbrush already laid out on the dressing table. An antique set of silver-backed brushes and cosmetic jars adorned the polished wood, and Davina brushed her hair automatically, her ears alert for any sound from Jamie's room. Her hair curled naturally and needed very little care apart from conditioning and generous brushing. It floated on her shoulders like a silken net as she padded across to the bed, taking care not to disturb the motionless figure lying on the opposite half of it as she slid back the covers and slipped down inside the cool freshness of soft linen sheets. During the nine months of their marriage she and Ruy had never slept together for an entire night. He had had his room and she had had hers, and it struck her as incongruous that they should do so now, when they had never been farther apart.

Despite the good twenty-four inches between them, she could feel the heat emanating from his body, her own absurdly aware of the deep even rise and fall of his breathing, her mind tormenting her with memories of his smooth teak skin, laid like silk over bone and muscle, fragrant with the musky odour of masculinity. Her body was as tense as a coiled spring.

'Go to sleep, Davina.'

She had thought him asleep and the words startled her to the point of closing her eyes obediently, and cringing back to the edge of the mattress until she realised that he could not follow her across the space which divided them even if he wished to do so. He had hurt her more than any man had ever hurt her before or after; she should be rejoicing in his downfall, so why did she have this overwhelming urge to take him in her arms and hold him as she held Jamie after he had had a tumble, cradling him against her breast and kissing away the pain? As sleep stole over her she fought against the tide of knowledge that would not be denied. All the love she had once felt for Ruy was dead, completely dead, and nothing could ever resurrect it. But deep down inside her a small voice whispered softly, 'Liar', and there were tears on her face as she finally slid into oblivion.

CHAPTER FOUR

SHE awoke to brilliant sunshine streaming in through the uncurtained windows, and Jamie patting her gently but impatiently on the arm.

'Come and watch my daddy swimming,' he besought her impatiently. 'Quickly, Mummy, before he stops. He can swim even faster than Superman!'

The events of the previous day came rolling back. Blinking uncertainly, Davina stared at the dent on the pillow next to hers, where Ruy's dark head had lain. Was Jamie imagining things, or was she the one whose imagination was playing tricks on her? How could Ruy, confined to a wheelchair, be swimming?

'Quickly, Mummy,' Jamie demanded, imperiously tugging at her nightgown. 'Quickly!'

Her son was dressed, his hair brushed tidily and his shorts and tee shirt clean; his sandals properly fastened and the right buttons in the correct buttonholes, tasks of which Jamie was not quite capable as yet.

Someone had dressed him. She glanced round the bedroom and then gasped, pulling up the covers as Rodriguez walked in.

'Rodriguez, is my daddy still swimming?' Jamie demanded impatiently.

The manservant's smile for the little boy was particularly warm. Spaniards loved children, Davina acknowledged, and it was obvious from the unselfconscious manner in which Jamie was chattering away to him that they had become firm friends.

'Rodriguez helped me to get washed and dressed, after he had helped my daddy,' Jamie told her, explaining how it came about that he was up and dressed. 'You were still asleep, Mummy. I wanted to wake you up, but Daddy said to leave you. I'm going to have my breakfast on the patio with Daddy. We're having proper orange juice from real oranges, and then Rodriguez is going to show me where they grow . . .'

She should have been pleased that he was adapting so quickly, but she couldn't quite prevent the small stab of pain his words caused her. Almost overnight he had changed from her baby to an independent young man who preferred the company of his own sex to hers.

'Well, if we're having breakfast on the patio I'd better get up and dressed before I miss it,' she said with a cheerfulness she wasn't feeling.

'Yes, hurry,' Jamie instructed her. 'And come and watch us swimming. I'm going to swim too, Mummy. Daddy said I could if you were there to watch me. Rodriguez has found my ring . . .'

Swimming was Jamie's latest accomplishment and love. Davina had been taking him to the local baths for several months. The doctor had suggested that the exercise might help to build up the muscles which had become a little wasted during the long weeks of his illness.

She glanced at the manservant and as though he had read her mind he offered politely, 'I shall watch him for you, Excelentisima, until you are dressed and then I must get His Excellency's breakfast.'

The title fell unfamiliarly on her ears, even though she had grown accustomed to hearing it during the brief months of her marriage. No matter how close

Rodriguez might be to Ruy, Davina knew he would never dream of not using his title. It was a matter of pride—to them both. A Spaniard felt no sense of inferiority to someone of higher rank, Ruy had explained coolly to her when she had commented upon it, because in his eyes a man was measured in other ways, and had Ruy suggested that Rodriguez adopt a more familiar attitude towards him the manservant would have taken it as an insult; a suggestion that he considered himself inferior to his master and therefore in need of compensation for his inferior role, whereas in reality they were both men and equal therefore in the sight of God and each other.

Davina dressed quickly, pulling on a soft lilac tee-shirt which accentuated the colour of her eyes, and a pretty floral wrap-round skirt which emphasised her long slender legs and narrow waist. The outfit was simple and yet becoming, although she herself was unaware of it and pulled a slight face at her reflection in the mirror, remembering the couture gowns worn by her mother-in-law and Carmelita. Of course she could not hope to compete with them; but then why should she want to?

Head held high, she walked in the direction of the swimming pool. Although it was early in the day the air was warm, and the sun strong enough for Davina to find it necessary to perch her sunglasses on the edge of her nose as the clear, pure light bounced back off the surface of the water.

She could hear Jamie shrieking with laughter as she approached the pool, and as she rounded the corner she could see why. Ruy was playing with him, tossing him a huge brightly coloured beach ball, which Jamie's chubby, baby hands reached for impatiently whilst his inflated arm bands kept him afloat, Rodriguez's sharp eyes alert for the first sign of any danger.

Man and boy were both so engrossed in their game that at first they didn't see her. Watching them Davina felt her heart contract with an emotion she was reluctant to name. With the water running off the brown satiny skin, the thick dark hair plastered wetly to his skull, Ruy might have been the lover she had once known. Watching him cleave the water powerfully as he directed the beach ball towards Jamie she found it almost impossible to believe that he was actually paralysed; that those powerful brown limbs slicing the water were incapable of any feeling . . . of anything . . . She made a small choked sound in her throat, drawing the swimmers' attention to her. Jamie squealed excitedly. 'Look at us, Mummy, we're playing ball . . . Watch my daddy swim. He can swim faster than anyone else in the whole world . . .'

Darling Jamie. How readily he accepted Ruy's role in his life.

She could hear Rodriguez moving behind her, presumably going to get the breakfast now that she was here to watch over Jamie . . . and Ruy. In the water he had all the swift sureness of a fish, but out of it he was equally helpless. When she could see that Jamie was tiring she went to the edge of the tiled pool and leaned down, holding out her arms to him. His hair was as wet as Ruy's, plastered to a small skull which was an exact replica of his father's. He was beaming with delight when Davina lifted him out.

'Soon, I'll be able to swim as fast as my daddy,' Jamie told her as she started to towel him dry. She glanced over her shoulder, half expecting to see Rodriguez emerging from the house. When she had

crossed the patio she had seen the table already
prepared for their breakfast, and as she knew from
experience Ruy normally breakfasted on crisp, fresh
rolls and honey which did not take long to prepare.
Her own mouth was starting to water at the thought of
those rolls, fresh from the Palacio ovens. Jamie stepped
out of his brief trunks and Davina looked round for
his clean clothes before she remembered that he had
come out with the manservant.

'You stay here for a moment,' she instructed him.
'I'll go and bring your shorts and a tee-shirt.'

When she returned there was still no sign of
Rodriguez. Ruy was still in the pool, but as she walked
towards them a very young maid came hurrying towards her holding a tray. On it was a bowl and a packet
of cereal, and with smiles and gestures the girl indicated that it was intended for Jamie.

Requesting her to place it on the table Davina found
Jamie sitting patiently by the side of the pool, still
watching Ruy. In the strong sunlight his skin looked
almost unnaturally pale—a legacy of his illness—and
Davina covered his arms and legs with sunscreen
before dressing him and pulling a canvas sunhat firmly
down over his dark hair.

There was still no sign of Rodriguez. Ruy's robe
was lying over his chair, and Davina glanced uncertainly from it to the seal dark head at the other side of
the pool, wondering whether to go or stay. Watching
him moving so smoothly and effortlessly through the
water reminded her unbearably of those few brief days
of happiness she had snatched from the grasp of fate
before the truth had blotted out her foolish dreams for
ever. She herself had not been able to swim before she
married Ruy. She had always been slightly afraid of

the water; timid and nervous of the rare occasions when there had been school outings to the local baths, but Ruy had insisted on teaching her the basic strokes and now she enjoyed her weekly visits to the baths with Jamie, who had taken to the water like the proverbial duck. A trait he must have inherited from his father, Davina reflected, watching Ruy float lazily on the blue green surface of the water.

He rolled over suddenly and swam leisurely to the side, shaking the water off his hair, and out of his eyes, before opening them and staring up at her. From the look in his eyes Davina realised that he hadn't been aware of her presence until that moment. It was as though a mask suddenly came down over his face, turning it into a hard implacable barrier.

She looked round again for the manservant, and not seeing him hurried across to the patio, hoping to find him there with Jamie. The little boy was eating his breakfast and chatting to the maid who was watching over him, and in answer to her query concerning Rodriguez's whereabouts told Davina that she did not know where he might be. For a moment Davina nibbled her lip indecisively. She was sure that Ruy could not manage to get out of the pool by himself, and remembering his threats of the previous evening wondered if she was supposed to help him. But how could she lift a grown man who must be half her size again? The only thing she could do was to go back and tell Ruy that she would have to go and find Rodriguez.

When she reached the pool, she saw by some super-human feat of strength he had managed to pull himself out of the water and was lying face downwards on the paving by the poolside, water streaming off his body. He was so inert that for a moment Davina feared that he might have lost consciousness and she approached him tremulously, her eyes unwillingly drawn to the mahogany breadth of his back tapering to the lean waist and narrow hips. He moved, causing muscles to ripple sinuously beneath his skin, reminding her of how it felt to touch the bronzed flesh of his back before sliding her fingers round to clasp the breadth of his shoulders.

'Well are you going to stand there all day staring at me, or are you going to help? Anyone would think you've never seen a man before,' he jeered, his eyes wide open and fixed contemptuously on her face. 'What's the matter?' he demanded. 'What were you expecting? Some obscene deformity?' He stretched upwards reaching for his chair and Davina rushed instinctively to help him, grasping the taut flesh of his waist, and receiving a shock like a jolt of electricity through her own body for her pains. Beneath her outspread palms his flesh felt warm and damp. She could feel a strange, almost forgotten heat rising slowly inside her, curling demandingly through her stomach and making her tremble with the knowledge it brought. Tears filled her eyes, and she blinked hurriedly to try and banish them. What was wrong with her? She had learned her lesson, hadn't she? She was over Ruy. Over all that nonsense about loving him. So why did she have this overwhelming urge to let her hands wander at will over the raw silk flesh beneath them, to take away his pain and humiliation, and make him feel for her the burning desire she had never stopped feeling for him? She forgot that she was half supporting him as he leaned between her and the wheelchair, and her hands released his flesh as though it burned as the enormity of what was happening dawned upon her. She still loved Ruy, had never stopped loving him, in fact. She stared dazedly into space for several seconds, coming back down to earth as she heard Ruy curse and she saw the lines of pain etched deep into his face as he slumped over the chair.

'Damn you!' he swore at her as she hurried to help him. 'Haven't you done enough already? Have you any idea of what it means to a man when the woman he loves leaves him? Keep your pity, Davina. I don't want it,' he told her brutally. 'Physically I might only be half a man but mentally nothing has changed. I can still feel . . . still desire . . .' he emphasised while she stared uncomprehendingly at the purple graze along his abdomen, the flesh raw and puckered where it had been torn and mangled by some primitive force, before disappearing beneath the top of the brief black swimming trunks he was wearing.

When she looked away she was white and trembling.

'So it sickens you, does it?' Ruy demanded harshly. 'You cannot feel desire for a man whose body is torn and mutilated. You prefer the smooth, pale skin of your Englishman. Get out of my sight,' he demanded bitterly. 'I have endured enough for one day, without being forced to endure any more.'

She went, on legs that threatened to give way beneath her. For a moment, after the first horror of his appalling scar had left her, she had longed to bend her head and place her lips to the ravaged flesh, to heal with the benison of her kiss the pain which she could only guess at, but it wasn't her kiss Ruy's heart and soul cried out for; it wasn't her love and compassion he desired. Hadn't he just accused her of pity?

She couldn't face any breakfast. She went straight to the bedroom, but the maids were working there, so she was forced to return to the patio, where she found

Jamie chatting to his grandmother, and Ruy calmly eating his breakfast, as though nothing untoward had occurred at all.

'This afternoon we are going shopping,' the Condesa informed Davina as the maid poured her a cup of coffee. 'As Ruy's wife you will have a certain position to maintain, and it is only fitting that you should be dressed accordingly.'

'It really isn't necessary,' Davina started to protest, but Ruy cut in cruelly, 'You can say that, when you are dressed in garments most of our maids would scorn—what manner of woman are you, Davina, that you conceal your body in such things? Or is it that you do not care how you dress when there is no man to impress?'

'That's a hateful thing to say . . .' There were tears in her eyes; tears of pain and tears of pride. Perhaps her clothes weren't elegant or expensive, but they were all she could afford.

'Next month we shall be entertaining visitors from Madrid—men connected with the wine business, and I shall want my wife to be dressed as befits her position. However, before that I must visit the *estancia*. The young bulls should be ready soon, and I must check on . . .'

'No, Ruy, let Sebastian go in your stead, *por favor*,' his mother begged, her face paling suddenly at his words. 'There is no need for you . . .'

'You would have me hide behind my little brother?' Ruy's face had darkened, his fist smashing down on to the table, making the crockery jump. 'Enough, Madre. I am still the head of this family, and if I say I shall go to the *estancia*, I shall go. Davina and Jamie will come with me. It is time my son learned how we derive a part of our income.'

Before his mother could protest further, he had turned away and was wheeling himself quickly towards his suite.

Giving her mother-in-law time to recover herself, Davina poured herself another cup of coffee, and assured Jamie that his daddy wasn't cross with him.

'It is my fault,' the Condesa said. She lifted her coffee cup and Davina was dismayed to see that her hand trembled. What had happened to the formidable woman who had seemed such an ogress such a very short time ago? All at once Davina was seeing her with her defences down, as a mother whose child was badly hurt and who was rejecting her. 'But he is so proud and I am so very worried. It was at the *estancia* that he received the wound and the fall which paralysed him. He was gored by one of the young bulls,' she told Davina quietly. 'An accident. One of the young boys ignored an instruction and the bull broke free. Ruy was only there by chance . . .' Her voice faded away, and Davina saw tears shimmering in her eyes. She felt like crying herself. Ruy, the proud and strong, to be reduced to dependence upon other human beings, and desertion by the woman he loved. If only he might have loved her! Her heart swelled with the intensity of her pain. Even without the bonds of physical pleasure she still loved him, and would have been proud to stand at his side. Ruy crippled was a thousand times more of a man than any other she knew; a thousand times more worthy of the name than others.

'You can see why I do not wish him to go to the *estancia,* but with you with him, and Jamie, he will not . . .'

She could not go on, and Davina turned to her with

shocked disbelief in her eyes. She could not believe
her mother-in-law was actually suggesting that Ruy
might be driven to making an end to his own life, but
the words lay unspoken between them and she knew
that this was the fear lying heaviest upon the other
woman's heart—and now upon her own. If necessary
she would stick to Ruy's side night and day to prevent
such a thing happening.

'I can never forgive Carmelita for deserting him
now, when he needs her the most,' Davina told her
quietly. 'To throw Ruy's love back in his face now . . .'

She was aware of a curious expression on the other
woman's face. 'Davina . . .' she began hesitantly, but
Jamie suddenly demanded her attention and when
Davina was able to turn back to her mother-in-law,
the latter commented that they had best hurry if they
were to reach Cordoba before the siesta. Sebastian and
Rosita, she explained, were to leave that afternoon on a
visit to Rosita's family, and if Ruy insisted on going to
the *estancia* then she would go to Cadiz to stay with
her sister for a short time.

'She has recently been widowed and very much
misses her husband . . .' She glanced at Davina. 'Now
that you have seen what has become of Ruy, Davina,
are you prepared to stay with him, as his wife, to bear
the brunt of his bitterness and anger, for the rest of
your life?'

Davina could not look at her. 'We are married,' she
said simply, and then holding her head high added,
'And I still love him, how could I not stay?'

Once admitted the truth seemed to release its crushing grip of her heart a little. Of course she loved him,
and had never stopped doing so no matter what she
might have told herself. In England's temperate clim-

ate her love might have gone into hibernation, deceiving her that it was dead, but beneath the warm, sunny skies of Ruy's home, it was growing again, reaching out to the warmth and sunshine. If she could persuade Ruy that life was still worth living, that she loved him paralysis or not, perhaps together they might be able to rebuild something. She was not Carmelita and never could be, but she was the mother of his child, and she loved him—enough for both of them? That was something she dared not ask herself.

Jamie was left with Ruy and Rodriguez while Davina and the Condesa went on their shopping trip. At first Davina had been reluctant to leave the little boy, so soon after their arrival, but sensing her hesitation Ruy had sneered harshly, 'Don't worry. Rodriguez will be here to watch over him, and unlike me he has the ability to follow his every move.'

'He is very precious to me,' Davina said simply, thinking but not saying that he was all she had of his father.

'You surprise me,' Ruy threw at her over his shoulder as he wheeled round abruptly. 'In view of your lack of feeling for his father and your marriage.'

She wanted to cry out that he was wrong, more wrong than he knew, when he accused her of not caring about him, but pride tied her tongue. How could she admit her love to him now, knowing that all he cared about, all he craved for was Carmelita?

Cordoba was much as she remembered it, enchanting dusty alleys where the sun turned the stone molten gold and without too much imagination it was possible to imagine these streets as they had been when the Moors ruled here. Enchanting courtyards and grilled gateways attracted the eye at every corner, a reminder of the secrecy which was an inherent part of these people's legacy from the Moors. With a little additional effort Davina could almost believe that dark-eyed girls still sat behind those grilles awaiting the arrival of their cavaliers, even though Ruy had told her that nowadays most young Spanish girls longed more for tee-shirts and jeans and boys on noisy scooters than serenades in the moonlight and courtship conducted with wrought iron between themselves and their admirers.

The Condesa did not waste time glancing in the windows of the small shops they passed—to Davina's eyes entrancing treasure troves of antique silver work and beautiful hand-crafted leather. Ruy had a saddle which had been presented to him by the gypsies who travelled across his lands every year on their pilgrimage to the Shrine of the Virgin. It was made of the softest, most supple leather Davina had ever seen in her life, embossed with silver and so heavy that when Ruy had handed it to her she had all but collapsed under its weight.

Every year during the annual Feria in Seville Ruy used the saddle when he took part in the horseback parade. The year of their marriage Davina had gone with him, and even now she could remember quite clearly the thrill of pleasure it gave her to see her husband dressed in the traditional Andalusian riding costume—the black Cordobes hat, frilled white shirt, short frogged jacket, red sash and narrow dark trousers. She had felt colourless against the Spanish girls in their beautiful dresses, riding pillion behind their menfolk, their flamenco dresses cascading in vivid rivulets against the sleek sides of their mounts.

Davina remembered that they had ridden down an avenue beneath scented white flowers of the acacia trees lining the streets. And after the parade there had been dancing—and what dancing! It went on without cease for three days and nights, Ruy had told her. She had not been able to join in because she did not know the steps, but Carmelita had been there to dance with Ruy, her scarlet skirts living up to her name as they danced breast to breast in the shadows.

She came back to the present with a sudden start as Ruy's mother directed her down a narrow flight of stone stairs to a small, enclosed patio, ornamented with pots of tumbling scarlet geraniums and bright blue lobelia. Elegant shutters kept the harsh sunlight off the windows, a gaily striped awning in black and gold throwing welcome shadows over the ground floor window, which the Condesa indicated that Davina was to examine.

'Concepcion is the daughter of an old friend of mine,' she told Davina. 'Her mother is disappointed because her daughter chooses to design clothes rather than marry, but girls these days do not heed their mothers as we had to. I have brought you here to see if perhaps we can find some clothes to suit your English colouring. Concepcion has travelled widely and this is reflected in her designs, so we shall see.'

Davina knew what the Condesa meant the moment they stepped into the small shop. Concepcion herself stepped forward to exchange lengthy greetings with the Condesa, leaving Davina free to examine the racks of clothes covertly—and acknowledge that her mother-in-law had chosen well. Here were all the colours of the rainbow, to suit her English fairness as well as the more olive-tinted Spanish skin. A pure silk dress with a tiny cinched-in waist and raglan sleeves piped in silver caught her eye and Concepcion smiled as they were introduced.

'That is one of my favourites too,' she told Davina. 'But pink is not often worn by my countrywomen. They prefer black even now. However, I am fortunate in having built up a clientele more modern minded than my mother's generation, and despite my parents' doubts since I opened this salon I have done quite well for myself.'

Davina could see why. The clothes a young salesgirl was discreetly displaying for her were mouthwateringly tempting. There was an evening dress in swirls of misty grey and lavender chiffon, which she knew the instant she saw it was made for her, elegantly simple day dresses in fabrics which whispered seductively against her skin when she tried them on. She would have been more than content with just a couple of items, but her mother-in-law insisted that she needed a completely new wardrobe. When Davina would have protested, she murmured in a brief aside,

'It is for Ruy. He is still very much a man, and it is only natural that he should want to be proud of his wife, that he should want to say to other men, this is my wife; she is beautiful and she dresses to complement her beauty for my appreciation. Continue to wear the clothes you brought with you from England and you might as well tell all Cordoba that you feel nothing for him. No woman who truly desires a man would dress for him in clothes such as you wear.'

By the time Davina had recovered her wits, two more evening dresses had been added to the steadily growing pile, and in her heart of hearts she knew that nothing would give her greater pleasure than to be able to wear these seductive, feminine clothes for Ruy's appreciation. Even though she knew that it would be

Carmelita he would be thinking of? a tiny cruel voice asked her.

'My parents are giving a party to welcome my brother and his wife home from South America,' Concepcion told them as they were on the point of leaving. 'I know they would be delighted to see you all there, and to make the acquaintance of Ruy's wife. It is good when all misunderstandings are past,' she added simply. 'Sometimes it takes a tragedy such as Ruy has experienced for us to realise the true importance of other people to us.'

It was only when they had left the small boutique that Davina realised that Concepcion thought that she had returned to Ruy because of his accident; and she wondered exactly how her absence in the intervening years had been explained away to their friends. For some reason she had thought that their marriage was something which would not have been discussed amongst their acquaintances—as far as Ruy was concerned it had been a mistake, and all he had wanted to do was to put the whole thing behind him and start again with Carmelita, or did his pride prevent him from admitting to outsiders now that the woman he loved had left him, and so he was obliged to fall back on the woman who was tied to him by law.

A chauffeur-driven car was awaiting them in the small square appointed as a rendezvous. It was extremely pleasant to settle back against the leather upholstery amidst air-conditioned comfort and be swept back towards the Palacio. Behind them lay Cordoba, the city of Abderrahman, the one-eyed red-haired giant, who had won a throne in the West for the Omayyad family of Damascus, and who had built around it a city of a million inhabitants, with a drainage system that could not be rivalled today, and street lighting a thousand years before any other European city, and of course, its Mosque.

The men who had fought with Abderrahman for the rich prize of Andalucia were the same men whose blood flowed through the veins of Ruy, neither tamed nor subdued by a thousand years of Christian rule and intermarriage with their Spanish captives.

Jamie was just waking up from his afternoon sleep when they got back to the Palacio. He already seemed to have wound the household round his little finger and when Sebastian and Rosita came to say goodbye to them, Davina thought she saw tears in the younger girl's eyes as she kissed Jamie on the forehead.

'You are lucky,' she told Davina softly. 'I would give much for such a son . . .'

'*You* are lucky,' Davina countered with a smile. 'I would give much to be loved as you are, Rosita . . . to have a husband who cares for me as Sebastian cares for you.'

When Davina went to her room to change for dinner, she found Ruy already in the room, lying back against the pillows of the double bed, his torso darkly tanned against the linen sheets. His eyes were closed and when Davina looked more closely, she could see the lines of pain etched beside his mouth and across his forehead and she had an almost overwhelming desire to reach out and stroke away the frown lines.

It was just as well she hadn't given way to it, she thought seconds later as the black lashes fluttered upwards and the dark eyes raked her assessingly, completely wiping out the impression of vulnerability she had had only seconds before.

'Aren't you coming down to dinner?' She knew it

was a stupid question the moment she uttered it. It was quite obvious that Ruy was in some sort of pain. Beneath his tan his skin had a faintly grey cast and now that she was looking at him properly she could see the tight white line of physical strain round his mouth, his knuckles gleaming whitely through his skin as his fingers clenched on the bedclothes.

'Why? Will you miss me?' he taunted. 'You could always stay here with me, if you really cared one way or the other, but we both know that you don't give a damn, don't we, Davina? If you did you'd never have walked out on me in the first place, would you?'

'You know why I did that,' Davina choked, turning her back on him, so that he couldn't see her expression and guess at the agony that decision had caused her. She still had her pride—for what it was worth.

'Yes, of course.' All at once he sounded oddly tired, defeated was the word she would have used in conjunction with another man, but it was unthinkable to use it for him. 'And we both know the folly of trying to preserve a marriage where one loves and the other merely ... endures ...' he added cruelly. 'So why did you come back?'

She took a deep breath, trying to steady her nerves. 'Because of Jamie,' she told him steadily. Well, it had been the truth after all. When she had decided to return it had been for Jamie's sake. She had honestly not known then that she still loved him so completely; or if she had, her subconscious had craftily kept the knowledge from her until it was too late for her to do anything about it. 'He was very ill last winter—enteritis, with complications, and the doctor told me that he needed to live somewhere warm ... to build up his reserves. I couldn't afford to take him abroad ... I earn enough to feed and clothe us but . . .'

'If you were so short of money, why have you never touched the allowance I make you?' Ruy demanded harshly.

He sounded so close that for a moment she had almost believed that he was standing behind her, but when she turned swiftly, he was still lying on the bed, his eyes burning into her like living coals. She hadn't touched the money because she had told herself that she wanted nothing of his, nothing at all, except his love.

'I couldn't,' she said simply.

'I see.' The effort of controlling his breathing showed in his tense muscles and dilated nostrils. 'But yet you were willing to return here and live on my charity . . .'

'I was frightened that if I didn't come you would try to take Jamie away from me. He is your heir after all. And . . .'

'You have talked to him about me?' he demanded abruptly, startling her. 'He knew I was his father . . .'

'He knew that we were coming to see his father,' Davina corrected. 'I've never lied to him about you, Ruy, nor tried to pretend you didn't exist, but neither have I told him a great deal about you. I thought it best, after all . . .'

'You never expected that I would play a significant part in his life, that's what you're trying to say, isn't it?' he goaded.

What could she say? That she had not wanted Jamie to endure the humiliation of knowing his father preferred the children he had given to another woman; that he hadn't been wanted; that his father had never even come to the hospital to see him; that he had been too busy making love to his mistress to bother about his wife and newborn son? These were not things you could tell a child, not even an adult, and if she had not talked to Jamie about his father, it had been from a desire not to taint his mind and heart against him, rather than with any thought of maliciously concealing Ruy's existence from him.

'I thought you would marry Carmelita,' she said quietly. 'After all, it was what your family wanted.' And what *you* wanted! The words trembled on her tongue, but she could not utter them, could not remind him of all that he had lost. Loving someone was an agony that made their pain your pain, only intensified tenfold, and she knew that if by some means it were possible to restore Ruy to full health and give him back Carmelita's love, she would have done so.

'Ruy . . .' Her voice faltered as she turned and saw that he was lying with his face turned away from her, the high cheekbones thrusting through the bronzed flesh, his eyes closed in total rejection of her.

She changed in Jamie's room, reading the little boy a story, before tiptoeing through the room where Ruy lay asleep to go and eat a meal she did not want, with her mother-in-law.

CHAPTER FIVE

THE bedroom was in darkness when Davina returned, Ruy a motionless shape in the vastness of the bed that had been designed generously to hold a couple who would and laugh and cry together all their lives. She averted her eyes from it and from the man lying there, the sheet pulled down to reveal the muscular darkness of his back, the broad shoulders tapering downwards to the narrow waist.

Quickly Davina hurried into Jamie's room. The little boy was curled up beneath the bedclothes still clutching his much beloved teddy. She bent to kiss him, straightening with tears in her eyes as she tried to blot from her mind the man lying in the bedroom opposite.

Not even the stinging spray of the shower dispelled the emotions that had surged up inside her when she looked at Ruy. She had had an insane desire to go to him and curl up against the protection of his body willing it to respond to her presence. Such wayward thoughts could cause her nothing but agony. There was no place in Ruy's life for her as a lover; indeed, it seemed that he could barely tolerate her there in any capacity. Sometimes when he looked at her she thought she glimpsed hatred in his eyes. The towel with which she was drying herself fell to the floor unregarded. Did he hate her? She pulled on her robe blindly. She had left her nightgown in the bedroom, but it didn't matter. There was no possibility that Ruy might inadvertently look upon her nakedness—even if he were to wake up she felt sure he would feign sleep as he had done before dinner.

With a small sigh she walked through into the bedroom, her unslippered feet making no sound on the cool tiles. Beyond the huge windows lay the gardens with all their fragrant intoxication, and her heart rebelled at the knowledge that she would never again walk in them with Ruy, never again lie with him beneath the stars never ... A sob rose in her throat, ruthlessly silenced by the small white teeth biting so deeply into her lip that it bled. Who were her tears really for? she asked herself. Ruy, because he would never walk again, or herself because she would never know his love?

There was no sign of her nightgown, and rather than risk disturbing Ruy by searching through her drawers for a clean one, she decided to sleep without. The cool crispness of the linen sheets stroked her naked skin like the hand of a lover. Sleep had never been farther away. Light from the crescent moon filtered through the windows, touching gentle silver fingers to Ruy's face, and clearly revealing the lines of suffering marked on it. An impulse which would not be denied had her reaching out trembling fingers to trace the path of the moonlight over the hard warmth of his skin. Surely it wasn't just her imagination that told her that the high cheekbones were sharper than she remembered, the skin tauter. Ruy moved and she withdrew her hand quickly, dismayed by the reaction of her flesh merely to the touch of his. Even her bones felt as though they were melting in the fierce heat of her hunger for him.

For nearly four years she had lived the life of a nun and never once after the first initial agony of parting from Ruy had she allowed her physical hunger for him to disturb her, and yet now, within forty-eight hours of her entering his house, her heart and body craved the close communion she had once known with him, to such an extent that merely to lie motionless at his side was almost a physical pain, and that was knowing that he did not want her; that he did not love her. There was neither rhyme nor reason to it; no sense in loving someone who loved elsewhere, and lying next to him, with her senses alive to the proximity of him, Davina found herself praying for the self-control not to reach out and touch him. Not to betray to him how she felt.

In the darkness she felt him move, tensing every muscle against her own involuntary reaction. His eyes opened, and he thrust back the sheets, muttering something under his breath, obviously unaware that she was there.

He rolled over on his side, reaching for the carafe of water by the bed. Davina heard the telltale rattle of pills as he picked up the bottle and then a bitter curse as he tried to pull himself upwards and knocked over the water jug.

Davina was out of bed, and at his side almost immediately, pulling on her robe as she hurried towards him.

'Mind the glass!' he warned her savagely. 'Don't come any nearer. Send for Rodriguez.'

'It's nearly one o'clock in the morning,' she told him calmly, 'and there's no need to disturb Rodriguez.'

In the kitchen she found a small brush and pan with which to clean up the mess. When she hurried back into the bedroom Ruy had switched on the bedside light, but its soft glow could not hide the pain in his eyes and the deep lines of strain etched on his skin.

The bottle of pills had crashed to the floor with the

water, and as she bent to pick them up Davina glanced at the label.

'Painkillers,' Ruy told her abruptly, as she replaced them on the cabinet. 'My wound still sometimes bothers me.'

Davina remembered her mother-in-law telling her that the wound had not healed as quickly as it should and that Doctor Gonzales had left a special cream to be applied to it when it proved especially painful. A quick glance at Ruy's face told her that now was one of those occasions, and when she had cleaned up the splintered glass and water from the floor, she went into the kitchen and quickly made a hot milky drink which she took back to Ruy and handed to him in silence.

'What is this?' he jeered. 'Have you discovered some long-buried desire to play the nurse?'

'I thought it might help you sleep,' Davina said quietly, adding before he could guess at the feelings which motivated her, 'If you're restless it keeps me awake too.'

'Meaning that if I were a gentleman I would allow you to have your own room, I suppose?' He looked bitterly angry; so angry that Davina couldn't help wondering if he was remembering that Carmelita had refused to share his bed.

'Well, I'm not going to, Davina. You're my wife, and you'll sleep in my bed, and that's an end to the matter. Where are you going?' he demanded sharply as she walked past him towards the bathroom.

'To find the cream for your wound.'

If she said it very matter-of-factly he would never know what it did to her insides to think of touching his body, even in the most clinical of ways, but the bitterness in his face undermined her resolution, and she had to look away from the hatred she saw in his eyes. Did he hate her so much that even the thought of her touching him could affect him like that?

She found the cream without difficulty, and although Ruy protested that he did not need it, the pain evident in the tautening bones of his face, and the eyes he closed against her, said otherwise.

'*Por Dios*, then get it over with if you must do it,' he gritted at her when he realised that she was not going to be swayed. As she reached for the sheets, he suddenly switched off the lamp, plunging the room into darkness again.

It was easy to find the ridge of the scar even without the benefit of the light, but her fingers trembled uncontrollably as she spread the cream lightly over the flesh which felt hot and burning to her touch, willing herself not to be betrayed into turning the action into a caress as her fingers so longed to do. His stomach was as lean and taut as ever, but she might as well have been touching alabaster for all the reaction she evoked, but her fears that his paralysis was such that he was unaware of her touch were banished when he pushed her away with a muffled curse and said harshly:

'You tremble like a captive dove. Why? Does my torn body revolt you so much? Does your imagination relay to you the full horror of my wound even though you cannot see it?'

'It doesn't revolt me,' Davina said softly.

'Liar. I saw it in your eyes before.'

Very slowly but determinedly, like someone in a trance, Davina pushed back the sheet until the moonlight touched starkly upon the jagged pulsating scar, and then deliberately bent her head and placed her lips to it, moving gently along the angry length of it, until

Ruy's fingers bit deeply into her shoulders, dragging her upwards.

'*Por Dios!*' he groaned huskily, staring incredulously at her. 'What are you trying to do to me? Would you humiliate me still further?' He pushed her away with a rough movement, and she half fell against the bed, her robe parting to reveal the full curve of her breast, silvered where the moonlight stroked it. She felt Ruy's indrawn breath, the sudden tensing of his muscles as his hand reached out and touched her flesh. Her mouth was dry with mingled tension and anticipation as his fingers brushed her breast. She was shaking uncontrollably and so was Ruy, his face dark and tortured as though he struggled under some terrible burden. Davina could have moved away, but she didn't. For a moment the silence stretched between them, and then with a hoarse groan Ruy reached for her, pulling her down against him, his face buried in the silky curtain of his hair as his mouth sought and found the betraying pulse beating in her throat, before moving upwards to capture her lips, parting them with a savage hunger to match her own.

Carmelita, the past, were both forgotten. Her arms slid round the hard warmth of his back, clasping her to him, her lips parting willingly under the assault of the passion she could feel rising up inside him.

'You have driven me to insanity!' she thought she heard him whisper against her skin, as his hands cupped the full warmth of her breasts. 'God has taken so much from me, surely he will not deny me this.'

The words were lost, smothered beneath the intense pressure of his mouth as it closed over hers, blotting out everything by the ferocity of their mutual desire. Thought was a slow, painful process obliterated by the instant communication of lips upon lips, flesh upon flesh. His accident and its results were forgotten, swept away in the sheer joy sweeping through her at the mastery of his touch.

'*Dios*, I have denied myself too long,' Davina heard him say thickly as he stared down at the unashamed nakedness of her body. 'I have fasted and thirsted; deprived my soul and flesh, but no longer.' His eyes lingered on her soft curves, making her pulses race in answering passion, her body mutely pleading for his touch.

His tortured groan filled her with a fear that he meant to withdraw from her, and she reached up towards him, gasping in pleasure as his mouth found her breast, his touch piercing her with exquisite sensation which seemed to run like quicksilver through her body, building up into an excruciating ache at the pit of her stomach.

His name whispered past her lips in aching surrender, lips which she pressed in mute supplication to the warm flesh above her.

She could hear Ruy's harsh breathing in her ear, feel the tremors that shook his body, sweat beading on his skin as he suddenly wrenched himself away from her, grasping her wrists as he stared down into her pale face with tormented eyes.

'Physically I may still be a cripple, Davina,' he told her hoarsely, 'but I can still feel . . . I am still capable of acting the part of your husband.'

The coldness of his tone made her wince, and his fingers tightened cruelly round her flesh, the look in his eyes reminding her of the primitive blood that still flowed through his veins.

'You cringe,' he said savagely. 'And well you might.

I am not a child to be petted and cossetted with kisses of pity, Davina. I am a man with all a man's reactions. Do you understand what I am saying to you?'

Even if she hadn't understood the words, those moments in his arms had already communicated the knowledge to her, and her heart filled with love and despair. Carmelita's desertion must have hurt him bitterly. He was still a man, she knew that beyond any shadow of a doubt, but when she tried to tell him so, he pushed her away and said sardonically, 'I don't want your pity, Davina. And I don't think I need to tell you what I did want. Next time you feel like pampering me like a small child, you might remember that—or does it give you some sort of perverted enjoyment to know that you can arouse a man like me; a man who ought to be revolted at the thought of a woman touching his rotting carcase of a body.' He moved violently to one side of the bed, and winced in pain.

Davina wanted to tell him that he was wrong. That she was the one who needed pity, because she had actually wanted him to continue making love to her even though she knew that he felt absolutely nothing for her, but he was already reaching for his bottle of tablets, and he swallowed two quickly, lying back with his eyes closed, exhaustion a pale grey shadow beneath the dark skin,

'If I were Carmelita . . .' she began hesitantly, but he silenced her with a look as cold as ice and a cruel smile as he told her softly, 'But you are not, and she at least is honest about her revulsion for a man confined to a wheelchair instead of trying to conceal her feelings with mawkish sentiment—a grave fault of the English, and one to which they are much addicted. Witness their outrage at the corrida. The bulls do not want their pity. They go to a noble death. And I do not want yours.'

It seemed like hours before she could get to sleep. Those moments in his arms remained vividly etched on her mind, and even though she told herself that she was glad Ruy had stopped when he did, she knew it was a lie. She had wanted him to possess her, wanted to feel again the magic she had first experienced as his bride.

As before when she awoke she had the bedroom to herself. She found Ruy and Jamie already eating their breakfast on the patio.

'My daddy is going to take us to a place where they grow bulls,' Jamie told Davina as she sat down. 'When are we going?' he asked Ruy.

'Soon,' the latter promised him. 'You will enjoy it at the *estancia*, *pequeño*. There are other children there for you to play with.'

Jamie seemed pleased by this observation. He had few friends in the small village where they lived, and she remarked unthinkingly to Ruy, 'It is a pity he is an only one. I think it tends to make children too precocious,' blushing furiously as his eyebrows rose mockingly.

'Is that an observation or an invitation?' he asked coolly. 'If it is the latter, I thought I made my views clear to you last night.'

'Meaning that I could never hope to take Carmelita's place, I suppose,' Davina said bitterly, not caring how much she might be betraying.

'Carmelita is a sophisticated woman of the world who knows how to let a man down gently. I scarcely think that description fits you.' He was about to leave the table when his mother approached them, a stiff white invitation card in her hand.

'It is from Concepcion's parents,' she told Davina. 'An invitation to their party as she promised. You will go, Ruy?'

'Of course,' he agreed smoothly. 'I am sure they must all be longing to see the freak I have become, and of course the beautiful woman who has so nobly chained herself to me.'

'If only he could learn to accept!' the Condesa sighed when he had gone. 'I had hoped having you here . . .'

'Me?' Davina tried to smile. 'I'm afraid I'm more of a nuisance than a help. Having me here must constantly remind him of Carmelita, and all that he's lost . . .'

Her mother-in-law seemed deep in thought. She glanced up at Davina and was about to speak when one of the maids hurried towards them.

'Dr Gonzales is here,' she told the Condesa. 'He asks to see the Conde.'

'Dr Gonzales brought Ruy into the world,' the Condesa told Davina as they walked towards the house. 'He is a friend as well as our doctor, and I should like you to meet him.'

The Condesa introduced them, and then had to hurry away to the kitchen.

Left alone with the doctor, Davina found herself being studied by a pair of shrewd, button bright black eyes.

'So you are Ruy's wife,' he announced at last, with a smile. 'I did not make your acquaintance before because at the time of Ruy's wedding I was away in South America, visiting my son. However, I have heard much about you, and I confess to being . . . surprised . . .'

He took Davina's arm and led her on to the patio. 'You do not strike me as the sort of girl who would desert her husband to run off with her lover. You do not have the eyes for it. Yours are far too vulnerable.'

Was that what he had been told?

'I left Ruy because ... because I could no longer endure a marriage which was not founded on love. But there was no lover ...'

'So ... But now you are back to take your place at your husband's side. Tell me, do you find him much changed?'

'A little. He is very bitter, but that is only natural. To have lost the use of his legs, and the woman he loves ...'

'So you admit that love, or the lack of it, can have a profound effect upon our behaviour? That is good. Has Ruy told you much about his condition?'

'Only that he's paralysed,' Davina said, feeling a little puzzled. 'And of course I've seen the scar ...' She bit her lip, not knowing quite how to phrase the question she wanted to ask. 'Doctor, surely when one is paralysed there's no feeling ... no ... sensation, and yet Ruy experiences pain. 'I've seen him take pain-killers, and I know ...' she blushed, and fumbled awkwardly for the words. 'I know he's not totally without ... without physical feeling.'

To her relief the doctor did not press her to explain herself, merely pursing his lips and patting her hand reassuringly. 'You strike me as a sensible young woman. If you think Ruy can experience sensation, then I am sure you have excellent reasons for doing so.' His eyes twinkled and he added teasingly, 'I am very glad to hear that you do. Ruy is a very proud man, and the fact that you have been able to break down his barriers sufficiently for you to discover that his paralysis is not what it at first seems reassures me

considerably. Men are men, Condesa, whether they are
in wheelchairs or not. The simple fact of being
deprived of the ability to walk does not deprive them
of the curse of feeling. I confess when I heard that you
had returned my first feeling was one of concern—for
Ruy. A woman who turned from him in disgust, who
refused to accept that he still had great need of her—
more now possibly than at any other time, for when
else can a man—any man—truly transcend the physical
bonds that constrain us than at that moment of conse-
cration to love which sets the soul free? A small fore-
taste of heaven, or so the poets would tell us, and I
sometimes wonder if they are not right—— Such a
woman would have destroyed him, and it was such a
woman that I feared you to be. Instead I find you are
exactly the opposite.'

All this had been said on a much more serious note,
causing Davina to stop and stare curiously at her
companion.

'Let us sit down and talk together, you and I,' Dr
Gonzales suggested, indicating a stone seat set into a
low wall next to a circular pool where light and shadow
played unceasingly on the water, and koi carp basked
indolently beneath the lily pads.

'You have thought that perhaps another child might
do much to lift Ruy from his despondency?' the doctor
suggested. 'Oh, I know his mother persists in the belief
that there will be no more children, fed, I am sure, by
a certain person, who I am glad to say no longer holds
any sway in this household.'

'You mean Carmelita?' Davina smiled sadly. 'I
would love to have another child, but I doubt I shall
be granted the opportunity,' she said bluntly. 'Ruy has
already told me that I can't take Carmelita's place . . .'

'Take her place? But you have your own,' the doctor said vigorously. 'Come, you are letting Ruy's depression infect you. Has he discussed his accident with you at all?' he asked, changing the subject.

Davina shook her head.

'So. You do not know, then, that it is my opinion that this paralysis is psychosomatic—that is to say it is of the mind rather than the flesh, but exists physically nonetheless.'

Davina stared incredulously at him. 'You mean Ruy is not really paralysed?'

Dr Gonzales shrugged. 'Who is to say? Certainly there is no organic reason why he should not walk. The spinal column is still intact; the muscles were torn but are now repaired, but it is the mind that controls our will. In Ruy's case there is what you might call a mental block, a refusal to accept that he is unharmed. The goring by the bull, the fall from his horse, all these are shocks to the system. A similar shock—a traumatic experience, as you would perhaps call it, this might sweep away the block that prevents him from walking.'

'And Ruy knows this?'

The doctor spread his hands expressively.

'I have told him, yes, but he does not choose to believe me. It is quite common. As I have said, Ruy is a proud man. He does not care to think that his subconscious is the master of his body, although it is so with all of us. And forgive me for saying so, but Ruy has more reason than most to suffer in this way. Has he not already lost the woman he loves—his child?' he demanded, when Davina looked puzzled.

He was, she realised talking about her; attributing at least a part of Ruy's condition to her absence!

'A proud man, who cannot tell the wife who has left him how bitterly he misses her, and the child she had borne him, what could be more natural than that he should find a more subtle means of telling her that he wants her to return?'

When Davina stared at him, he smiled. 'You do not believe me, I can see, but think about it. It worked, did it not? Subconsciously Ruy called to you, and you responded.'

'As any woman would have responded,' Davina began helplessly, unbearably tempted to allow herself to believe that he was right, that Ruy had wanted her, even while she knew in her heart of hearts that it could not be so.

'Not any woman,' Dr Gonzales corrected her. 'A very special woman. One who appreciates that her husband is still a man . . . still has a very great need of her.'

'If you were right, surely now that I have returned Ruy would recover,' Davina pointed out logically, but the doctor only smiled again and shook his head.

'If only it were as simple as that! These deep workings of our subconscious are something even modern medicine cannot totally understand. We know that it does happen, we know how much power the subconscious can exert over the body, and even in what circumstances that power can be reversed, but what we do not yet know is how! We cannot simply tell the subconscious to release its hold of the body—or of the mind in the case of amnesia—we can only provide it with the right sets of circumstances and hope that they will act as a trigger. Either Ruy's subconscious will not heed the trigger or he still fears deep down inside that perhaps you will leave him again. To his subconscious it might appear that you will stay with him only while he is helpless, and thus he will remain.'

'And the other thing you were telling me about,' Davina questioned him, 'the traumatic experience which might free the mental block?'

It was pointless telling the little doctor that she could not be the cause of Ruy's paralysis, simply because he did not love her, for she was sure he would not believe her.

'Ah yes ... So much danger surrounds such a method of treatment that we doctors are reluctant to advocate it. In Ruy's case, for instance, such a shock treatment might require him to be gored by a bull for a second time.' He shrugged and grimaced slightly. 'If he did not die from the goring there is no guarantee that it would work, and so you can see that as a cure it is not particularly reliable.'

Davina could well appreciate why. She had read of such cases, especially where amnesia was concerned, where people had lost complete decades of their life only to find them returning after some chance meeting with someone from that previous, forgotten, life. She had even read once about a deaf man suddenly recovering his hearing after standing too close to a jet aircraft preparing for take-off, but as Dr Gonzales said, the risks of such hit-and-miss treatment were too great for any professional man to suggest that a patient take them.

He came every other day, he told her a few minutes later, but she declined to accompany him to Ruy's room, knowing that Ruy would not want her present when the doctor examined him.

She could not understand why Carmelita had turned away from Ruy and married someone else, unless it was as she had suspected before, that the other girl's pride would not allow any child of hers to take second place to Jamie, and so she had used Ruy's accident as an excuse to put an end to their relationship. Despite her comments to the contrary, Davina had never thought that Carmelita truly loved Ruy—not as she loved him—and she longed to go to him and tell him that no matter what might happen in the future, he would always have her love to call on should he need it. But that was the point, wasn't it? He didn't need it. All he wanted was Carmelita!

CHAPTER SIX

HER skin was beginning to tan already, Davina noticed appreciatively as she slid on one of her new dresses. She was changing in Jamie's room, ostensibly so that the little boy could see her in her new finery, but in reality she hadn't been able to endure the feel of Ruy's critical eyes on her, nor his own torment as he waited to be dressed as helplessly as any child.

Only that lunchtime he had thrust her away from him when, unable to watch him struggling any longer with the shirt he was endeavouring to pull over his shoulders, she had run to his side to help him. It would be a long time before she forgot the raw fury in his eyes as his fingers locked on her wrists in a grip that had left purpling bruises on her smooth flesh. She glanced down at them now, a tiny frown creasing her forehead as she touched the swollen flesh. Why did he insist on tormenting both of them in this fashion? It was plain that he hated her witnessing his disability, and yet when she had tentatively suggested that they have separate rooms after all, he had told her in a cold fury that as long as she remained under his roof she would share his bed, adding cryptically that it was a penance for them both.

Davina had dressed for tonight's party with special care, remembering what the Condesa had said about their hosts being importantly placed in Cordoban society.

The dress was one of Concepcion's creations, a misty

froth of chiffon in pearl greys and soft lilacs, the boned bodice emphasising the taut thrust of her breasts before hugging her narrow waist and falling to the floor in graceful folds. There was a matching jacket to go with it, with a tiny stand-up collar and tight sleeves, and as she applied a hint of pearlised lilac eyeshadow to deepen the amethyst of her eyes, she had to admit that she had never owned a dress which became her so well.

'Mummy smells nice,' Jamie commented when she touched perfume to her pulse points before slipping into her high-heeled evening sandals.

As she bent down to give the little boy a last-minute hug she heard the bedroom door open. When she straightened up Ruy was behind her, looking immaculate in a crispy laundered white shirt and narrow hip-hugging black pants. Not even being confined to a wheelchair could really rob him of his vitality, Davina thought, suppressing a longing to reach and cradle his dark head against her breast as she had done Jamie's.

'Mummy smells nice,' Jamie repeated for his father's benefit.

'So I notice. They say a man can learn a good deal about a woman by her choice of perfume.'

Davina wore Chamade. The first time she had ever worn it had been on the day they got married. Ruy had given it to her as a present, and her face flamed at the thought of what her wearing of it now might betray.

'In your case it betrays a lack of sensitivity which is staggering,' Ruy continued bitterly. 'Or don't you think a woman should feel sentimental about her first lover and the gifts he gives to her?'

'Why should she?' Davina demanded before she

could stop herself. 'When he intends those gifts for someone else?'

She turned back to the mirror and busied herself applying her lipstick, firmly ignoring the trembling of her hands and the uneven pounding of her heart. Why did he insist on torturing her in this fashion, or was he using her as a substitute for Carmelita, taking out on her all the bitterness he could not give vent to elsewhere?

She didn't see him again until she went into the main *sala*. His mother was talking to one of the maids, and as she walked into the room Ruy beckoned her over, his face still grim.

When she was standing in front of him he flicked open a small black velvet box to reveal, embedded in white satin, a pair of diamond and pearl eardrops.

Davina knew at first glance that they were a family heirloom. The pearls were huge, the setting old-fashioned.

'It is customary for these to be presented to the wife of the Conde on the birth of their first child,' Ruy told her emotionlessly. 'Madre was kind enough to remind me that our friends would expect to see you wearing them tonight.'

The look he gave his mother was no kinder than the one he had given Davina, but the Condesa seemed better able to withstand it, for she shrugged carelessly and asked him if he was not going to put the earrings on for Davina.

'But of course. Provided she doesn't mind kneeling on the floor at my feet so that I can do so. It would be best for us all, Madre, if you ceased this folly of pretending that I am as other men, when the very evidence that I am not stands before you in the shape of my oh, so beautiful and faithless wife.'

'Ruy!'

The warning in his mother's voice was ignored, and for the first time Davina saw the older woman quail before his anger.

'You take too much upon yourself,' he said harshly. 'And I have said nothing—but listen well, Madre. I will no longer tolerate your interference in my life. Yours or anyone else's,' he finished pointedly, his eyes on Davina.

Davina could only admire the other woman's superb self-control. Not so much as by a flicker of an eyelash did she display any emotion, but Davina was sure she had seen the betraying glisten of tears in her eyes before she calmly turned away.

There was a gilded rococo mirror in the *sala* and Davina stood almost on tiptoe to see into it as she clipped the heavy earrings on to her ears. As she moved her head the diamonds flashed blue-white fire, the pearls reflecting the subtle lilacs and greys of her dress, but magnificent though they were, Davina would much rather not have worn them. She was terrified that she might lose one or damage them in some way, and as she followed the others out to the car her fingers strayed constantly to her ears to make sure that they were still in place.

'Before the winter Ruy must buy you some furs,' the Condesa commented as the chauffeur opened the rear doors of the car. 'I still have the sables his father bought for me.'

'What are you trying to do, Madre?' Ruy asked cynically from the shadows. 'Persuade Davina to stay with the promise of a reward for good behaviour? Perhaps already she grows tired of her life sentence

and looks forward to the time when she may be free of
it.'

'No . . . that's not true!'

Ruy turned to stare at her, his lips twisted in a
mocking smile.

'I think I preferred you when you were indifferent
to me, Davina. At least then you were being honest. I
cannot see what the point is of this pretence of caring
about me, unless it is that you enjoy torturing me . . .
causing me pain. Get in the car, Madre, we are already
late, and we do not wish to keep the other guests waiting, especially when we are the star turn.'

There had been a grain of truth in Ruy's sardonic
statement, Davina acknowledged an hour later, making
polite small talk with the gentleman seated to her left.
From the moment they had entered the *sala* Davina
had been subject to courteous but thorough inspection.

'Pay no heed to them,' Concepcion had murmured
gaily to Davina just before they went into dinner.
'They have nothing else to occupy their minds.
Whenever my mother bewails my unmarried state, I
point to the daughters of her friends and ask if she
would really want such an empty featherbrain of a
child. Now I can see that I shall have to marshal fresh
arguments. Now that she has seen you I fear my days
of convincing her that marriage equals intellectual
death are at an end!' She had smiled to show that her
words had not been meant to be taken seriously, but
nevertheless they had warmed Davina's heart, making
her feel welcome in a house where everyone else
seemed to be viewing her slightly critically.

Ruy was obviously a great favourite with the other
guests, but beneath their kind questions Davina sensed

the well-meant pity that she knew must be like salt in Ruy's unhealed wounds. She glanced across the table, where he was deep in conversation with Concepcion. The other girl was laughing up into his face, and Ruy's mouth was curled in the teasingly mocking smile she remembered from their first meeting, his eyes crinkling at the corners, and all at once she was overwhelmed by a fierce rush of jealousy—jealousy that Concepcion should be the recipient of his smiles, when for her, his wife, he had nothing but harsh words and contempt.

After dinner Ruy disappeared with their host into the latter's study—'To discuss business,' Concepcion told Davina. Her father and Ruy had a joint interest in a new development of holiday apartments in a select part of Marbella and this was what they were discussing.

While Concepcion was telling her how charming she looked in her new dress, Davina became aware of a tall, darkly handsome man watching them. She glanced up quickly, flushing a little when he smiled, uncoiling his lean body from the wall and strolling across to join them.

'Ah, Carlos, you are making good use of Ruy's absence to make yourself known to his lovely wife,' Concepcion told the intruder. 'Davina, allow me to introduce you to my cousin Carlos. At the risk of swelling his over-large head even more I must tell you that Carlos is one of Ronda's most famous bull-fighters.'

Davina smiled shyly at him. He was about Ruy's age, and built in much the same mould, although he had a devil-may-care air that made her think that here was a man who lived from peak to peak, tasting only the sweet things of life. When he raised her fingers to his lips with old-fashioned courtesy and then lingered over their pink tips with a meaning that was decidedly modern, Davina gave him a reproving look.

'Ah, I can see that Davina has your measure, Carlos,' Concepcion, who had intercepted the look, chided. 'I must also tell you that Carlos is a terrible flirt . . .'

'You malign me,' her cousin contradicted, still holding Davina's fingers. 'It is just that I have not yet found the woman to make me forsake all others, and so, like a busy bee, I must flit from flower to flower, tasting them all . . .'

'Well, don't try any tasting on Ruy's preserves,' Concepcion warned him, much to Davina's embarrassment.

Far from being disturbed, Carlos merely laughed wickedly. 'A man may only trespass on private property when the fences are down and the gates left untended, is this not so, *señora*? Ruy does not strike me as a man careless enough to leave his property in such an uncared-for state.'

'My mother tells me that you and Ruy are shortly leaving for the *estancia*,' Concepcion interrupted firmly. 'You will enjoy it, I am sure. I remember visiting it once with my parents. In our cities we Spanish preserve formality with rigour, but in the country, life is more relaxed, more as you are used to in England. And best of all, you will have your husband and son to yourself, for Ruy's mother does not go with you, does she? A second honeymoon, yes?'

Davina managed a rather strained smile.

'Ruy wants to check on the young bulls,' she said hesitantly.

'And you fear another accident such as the one which has put my poor friend in that wheelchair?' Carlos suggested, misreading the reason for her hesitation. 'Ruy is a brave one, *pequeña*, but not, I think, a foolish one.' He smiled suddenly to someone behind Davina. 'Speak of the devil, is that not what you say in your country? Ruy, we were just talking about you,' he said to the man coming towards them. 'You are shortly to leave for your *estancia*, I hear? May I take the liberty of inviting myself to visit you?'

Ruy must be in pain, Davina thought worriedly. She had not seen his face looking so grey since last night. She was just wondering if she could discover discreetly if he had brought his painkiller with him when he said brusquely, 'If it is the bulls you come to see, Carlos, then you are welcome as always.'

A small smile played round Carlos' lips.

'Ah, that is one of the penalties of having a beautiful wife, *amigo*, it causes one's friends to break the tenth Commandment!'

Other members of the family joined them and the conversation became more general, but before they left Concepcion drew Davina to one side and said awkwardly, 'Forgive me if I presume, Davina, but I like you and think we could become good friends. I must admit at first I was prejudiced against you, but having met you . . . If you will take a little advice. Do not provoke Ruy's jealousy. On the surface I know he is all urbane sophistication, but this is just the covering, the velvet which clothes the steel; inside there is a man whose ancestors defied convention and law to obtain their desire. Ruy may not show it, but he is a deeply passionate man; to compare him to Carlos is like comparing a babbling brook to a bottomless lake, if you take my meaning. I would not what you think I am meddling,' she added hastily. 'Sometimes it is good for husbands to think they have a rival, this is something all women know, but there are other times . . .' She shrugged as though unable to find the words, and Davina said quietly,

'Ruy need fear no rival, Concepcion. Neither your cousin nor any other man.'

'So. You and I know this . . . but does Ruy?'

There was silence in the car on the return journey. Davina felt drained of all energy, exhausted by the effort of continually smiling and answering questions.

'So Carlos is to visit the *estancia*,' the Condesa commented when the car drew to a halt in front of the Palacio. 'A charming young man . . .'

'Who has slain as many women with his *piropos* as he has bulls with his sword,' Ruy said dryly.

The Condesa shrugged. 'He is young, handsome and famous, it is natural that girls should admire him—do you not think so, Davina?'

'Yes, Davina,' Ruy goaded, 'do tell us what you think, or can we guess? I believe my delightful wife was quite blinded by the light of admiration shining in Carlos' eyes.'

'Nonsense,' Davina said as lightly as she could. 'I'm not a fool, Ruy. Carlos was doing nothing more than passing a few idle moments. I've lived long enough to recognise flirtation from any stronger emotion.'

'And to recognise love when you see it?' Ruy said softly. 'But of course you can. How many men have loved you, Davina? Have been deceived by that air of outward purity and innocence?'

It was so unfair, Davina thought resentfully, when he had deliberately and coldbloodedly deceived her, letting her think that he actually loved her when all the time . . .

Rodriguez was waiting for Ruy in the *sala*, but he dismissed him. 'I have work to do before we can leave for the *estancia*. You need not wait up for me. The Condesa will do all that is necessary.'

'He must be in pain,' Ruy's mother confided to Davina when Ruy left them to go to his study. 'Often then he cannot sleep and works to ward off the agony of his wound. If only I could turn back the clock!'

'To before his accident,' Davina said, understandingly.

'And earlier still. Davina, perhaps you would be kind enough to pour us both a glass of *fino*. It has never been my habit to drink sherry before I retire, but tonight I am in need of courage, and perhaps a glass of the sherry matured in our own *bodegas* might help me to find it. But first, let me ask you a question. Why did you come back to Spain? Was it just for Jamie?'

Davina poured them both a glass of the pale dry *fino* and handed one to the Condesa before taking a chair opposite her. Only the lamps illuminated the room with its carved furniture and rich rugs. On the wall hung a portrait of Ruy's father, and she glanced up at it before speaking. He had died when Ruy was still at school, and from being a boy he had been forced to grow up almost overnight to assume the responsibilities that went with the title.

'No,' she said honestly at last. 'Oh, I told myself it was. I told myself that Jamie needed the mild climate; that it was his right . . . I had a thousand and one reasons why I should come here, but none of them entirely the truth, and even when I discovered that Ruy had not written to me, that he didn't want us, I couldn't go home. I couldn't find the pride to turn my back on him . . .'

'Because you love him . . . still?'

'Yes.' The sighed admission fell into the silence of the room. 'Yes, I love him, even now knowing that he cares nothing for me; that he truly believes me capable of passing off another man's child as his . . . that he didn't even care enough to come and visit me after Jamie's birth . . .'

'That wasn't his fault, Davina.'

'No? I saw the photographs of him at the *estancia* with Carmelita, remember? He was making love to another woman while I was bearing his child!'

'No.' The Condesa had gone pale. It seemed to Davina that she was steeling herself to speak. 'I took those photographs, with Carmelita's conniving. You see, Davina, I bitterly resented you for marrying my son. It had been an understood thing that he would marry Carmelita since they were both children, and then suddenly in one week all that was changed and he was married to you. I was very proud in those days and had yet to learn that man is no match for God. I was determined to break up your marriage. It could be set aside, I told myself. The Church would look favourably on a petition from a man of Ruy's standing—but then you conceived Ruy's child.

'It was Carmelita who thought of the plan. She encouraged Sebastian to gamble heavily at a casino in Marbella. All he had was his allowance from Ruy, and we timed it carefully so that Ruy would discover his brother's misdemeanours when you had to go into hospital. I assured Ruy that I would tell you why he could not be with you, why he had been called away. I had also let slip to him, as though by accident, that you were meeting an Englishman behind his back. My son has a jealous nature, although he conceals it well.

It was easy to drop the poison into his ear. Insecurity is an excellent breeding ground, and it wasn't hard to convince him that you had a lover—a man to whom you turned in his absence.

'It was Carmelita's suggestion that we show you the photographs. They had been taken the previous summer, but you too were uncertain and hurt because in your eyes Ruy had deserted you when you needed him.'

And hadn't loved her, Davina reminded herself. She mustn't lose sight of that; mustn't think just because the Condesa was telling her this now that it meant that Ruy felt any differently towards her. He still loved Carmelita.

'Thank you for telling me, but you must see that it can't make any difference now, although it does help to explain why Ruy seems to think that I've had a chain of lovers in and out of my life since we parted.'

'And why he did not show any interest in Jamie, although to look at the *pequeño* is to know that he is a Silvadores . . .'

But if Jamie had taken after her in looks, what then? Davina couldn't help asking herself. Still, it was pointless to speculate.

'It has lain on my conscience since your return,' the Condesa continued. 'You are Ruy's wife—a far better wife to him than Carmelita could ever have been—and Jamie is his son. I hope you can forgive me, Davina.'

'For what?' Davina smiled bleakly. 'What happened would probably have happened anyway. I'm only sorry that Ruy had to be disillusioned about Carmelita. Her defection must have hurt him.'

'You are a generous child,' the Condesa said softly, replacing her glass on the table. 'Perhaps now that I have sought absolution from you I can start to forgive myself. Will you tell Ruy?'

Davina shook her head.

'No. The past is dead, and as you say, no one looking at Jamie could doubt that Ruy is his father.'

Even so as she prepared for bed it was hard to tell herself that nothing could be gained from telling Ruy now what had happened all those years ago. It was true that the Condesa and Carmelita between them had done much to break up her marriage—had Ruy come to the hospital after Jamie's birth she would probably never have left him, and it was inarguable that Carmelita had deliberately made sure that he would not be with her, just as the Condesa had deliberately fostered the impression that she was having an affair with another man, but both of them had believed these deceits without question.

Hadn't Carmelita had enough with Ruy's love, without stooping to destroy whatever feeling he might have had for the wife he had taken in retribution? She could still remember how she had felt that day when Carmelita had told her that she and Ruy were lovers—had been lovers for some time, and were on the point of marriage until they quarrelled—facts which were borne out by the Condesa's information that there was an 'understanding' between the two families. Knowing that had robbed her of the ability to respond to Ruy with the passion his lovemaking had aroused inside her. She couldn't forget when he touched or held her that he loved another woman, and so eventually he had withdrawn from her and she had told herself that she was glad; that it was impossible for her to endure the degradation of being made use of merely because she was there.

She had just stepped out of the bath and was reaching for a towel when the bathroom door was suddenly pushed open. Knowing she was alone in the bedroom, she hadn't bothered to lock it. For what seemed like aeons she and Ruy stayed at one another and then, suddenly becoming aware of her nakedness, Davina grabbed for the towel, flushing furiously as his eyes made a slow appraisal of her body, lingering on the full roundness of her breasts. The effect was exactly the same as had he actually touched her. Her breath seemed to be lodged somewhere in her throat, her nipples hardening in immediate aroused enticement. She tried to cover her nudity with the towel, but Ruy was too quick for her. For all that he was confined to his chair he could manoeuvre it deftly, and when it came to a struggle she was no match for him. In seconds he had removed the towel from her grasp, placing it on his lap as he drawled savagely:

'Why should I not look at you? Why should I deny myself the pleasure you give so freely to others? Your body tells me that your thoughts were not those of an innocent. Of whom were you thinking? Carlos? Does it excite you to think of him coming to you with the blood of his bull still scarlet upon his hands?'

'Stop it! I won't listen to any more!' Davina clamped her hands to her ears, her face pale with shock and pain. 'I wasn't thinking of Carlos.'

'No?' The soft word was accompanied by a smile that sent chills down her spine. 'Then who were you thinking of—and do not tell me "no one".' He was moving towards her, forcing her backwards into the corner, until the walls brought her to an abrupt halt and she had no defences against the cruel stroke of his fingers along the thrusting outline of her breasts. 'I know well what this means,' he told her, caressing her erect nipple with his thumb. 'So, who were you thinking of when you looked in the mirror and saw the reflection of your own body; whose caresses were you imagining?'

'My lover's!' Davina flung at him, goaded beyond endurance, and after all, it was true. The person she had been thinking of had been him, and although he did not know it he had been her only lover.

'*Por Dios!*' A fury she had never seen before glittered in his eyes, and, thoroughly frightened, she tried to escape, but he was too quick for her, and her bare feet slipped on the tiles, causing her to fall against him.

'Your lover, you say?' Ruy ground out furiously against her ear. 'Well, as your husband, I must just see if I cannot give your wayward thoughts another direction, must I not?'

The moment he touched her Davina knew that she was lost. She could not fight his anger and her own desire. His touch kindled a fire that spread through her veins like melted honey, rendering her mindless and able only to obey an instinct which went deeper by far than reason or logic. With her body crushed against his, the buttons of his shirt tiny pinpoints of pain against her skin, she allowed him to explore and plunder as he wished, finding in her surrender a sweet agony which blinded her to everything but the need to prolong the pleasure of feeling his hands on her skin arousing feelings she had thought long dead, his lips sending spirals of pleasure through quivering nerve endings as they moved languorously along her throat and shoulders.

'You want me, Davina,' he said slowly, cupping her

face and forcing her to stare at her own aroused expression.

'And you want me . . .'

It was a statement of fact and one he didn't choose to deny. Instead he released her slowly and then started to remove his shirt, manoevring the chair forward.

Davina followed him. An intense ache built up deep inside her. The next move, if there was to be one, would have to come from her. Did she have the courage to openly solicit his lovemaking, knowing his desire was merely physical?

She had convinced herself that she had not when she remembered Dr Gonzales saying that another child might help to release Ruy's mental block. Like a sleepwalker she walked towards him, kneeling to unfasten the cufflinks gleaming palely gold in his cuffs.

He had gone completely still and when when she looked up at him his face might have been carved out of a block of stone.

'Make love to me, Ruy,' she said huskily. 'I want you.'

It was almost a relief to say the words, although what she should have said was that she loved him, but love was a word which must never be uttered between them.

When still he made no move towards her her heart plummeted downwards. Perhaps she had misjudged the extent of his need. It was hard to pull on her nightgown and pretend that nothing had happened, turning her back and closing her ears against the sound of him preparing for bed. His chair lifted to the height of the bed, enabling him to get from one to the other without help, and she felt the mattress depress as he rolled on to it.

His hands on her waist made her stiffen in shock.

'So you want me to make love to you? Why, so that you can add it to your lengthy list of "experiences"? Damn you to hell, Davina!' he swore suddenly, his mouth closing over hers. 'Well, if it's an "experience" you want, I'll make damn sure this is one you'll never forget!'

And neither would she, Davina thought pain-hazed seconds later as the clamped hands on her waist prevented her from moving and the oppression of Ruy's mouth forced the tender inner skin of her lips back against her teeth until she could taste blood. The full weight of his body held her pinned to the bed as the restricting nightgown was rent destructively from neck to hem to make way for hands which seemed to know exactly where to touch and torment, bringing her to the very edge of pleasure and then withholding it until her breath was a sobbed rasp in her throat. Time and time again his hands stroked across her stomach and beneath her ribcage, causing her to press herself against him in a frenzy of desire, her lips leaving moistly pleading kisses in the hollow of his throat and the breadth of his shoulders while her fingers curled protestingly into the muscles of his back, and her breasts ached for his possession.

As though he knew exactly what it was doing to her his hands cupped their heavy warmth and he lowered his head. Her stomach muscles tensed defensively, but it was no use. Even the merest touch of his breath against her skin betrayed her need, and when his tongue tormentingly circled first one tautly erect nipple and then the other she could barely prevent herself from crying out loud.

'I hope you're enjoying this experience, Davina,' she heard him mutter thickly as he lowered his full weight on to her and the ache in her stomach became a tormenting fever. 'I should hate to be in any way mediocre.'

She didn't want him to talk to her. Hearing him speak ruined the dream she had spun for herself that he actually loved her as she loved him; that the burning pressure of his lips was conveying more than mere desire and that the sudden tremors shuddering through him were not merely caused by physical desire.

She wound her arms round his neck, forcing herself not to beg him to give her his love.

'Please, Ruy . . .' It was near as she could come to an admission, but instead of complying with the soft plea, Ruy suddenly thrust her away, swearing savagely.

'No,' he said bitterly, 'I cannot do it. I will not compete with your other lovers, Davina. I may be a useless cripple, but I am still a man and not an animal!'

'But you wanted me . . .'

'For a moment, until I remembered how many other had also "wanted" you.'

'Ruy . . .' She reached out tremulously, intending to tell him the truth and that there had been no other man but him, but he thrust away the hand resting lightly on his chest as though it had burned and said thickly:

'*Por Dios*, do not touch me, or are you determined to drag me down to your gutter?'

Her tears soaked steadily into her pillow, making her throat ache with the effort of suppressing them. Never again would she allow Ruy to hurt her as he had done tonight. She had offered him her body out of love and desire, and he had turned that offer into something sordid and hateful. From tomorrow they would sleep in different rooms no matter what Ruy might say to the contrary; it was one thing to accept his bitterness and contempt, it was another to allow him to humiliate her as he had done tonight and for the sake of her sanity she could not allow it to happen again. He had quite deliberately aroused her—she was sure of that— she was even sure that he had intended to make love to her, but to be told that he could not do so because she disgusted him was something she would never recover from.

CHAPTER SEVEN

As he had business in Marbella, they would break their journey there and have lunch at the Yacht Club, before going on to the *estancia*, Ruy told Davina over breakfast.

There were still lines of pain etched heavily on the taut flesh of his face and she was worried that the long journey, plus the strain of sitting through an arduous business meeting, might be too much for him, but when she ventured to suggest that they dispensed with lunch and that instead he rested, his eyes darkened to the colour of obsidian, glittering with the anger which found an outlet in the ice-cold-voice with which he demanded if he was expected to believe that her 'concern' was truly altruistic.

'If you are ashamed to have lunch with me then you can always remain in the car. I will not be reduced to the life of a hermit simply because I no longer have the use of my legs.'

His twisting of her words infuriated Davina. When Jamie had toddled off with Maria to help 'pack his clothes' she rounded on Ruy, ignoring the implacable set of his mouth and the warning glint in his eyes.

'*You* are the one who insists that the loss of the use of your legs diminishes you as a man,' she told him, anger overcoming caution. 'From the first moment I arrived here you have insisted that in some way I relished your pain and disability, but this is just not so. You're the one who's enjoying it, Ruy. Dr Gonzales says there's nothing wrong organically; you could walk . . . but you refuse. If you want my view, I think you're deliberately trying to make me feel guilty, to make . . .'

She faltered to a standstill, horrified by what she had said. Ruy's face was as grey as the paving beneath their feet, and she longed to take back her impulsive words and tell him that they had been said in the heat of her anger, but she was not granted the opportunity. Struggling to pull himself out of his chair, supporting his weight on the table, he towered over her, his eyes raking her trembling body from head to foot.

'To make you what?' he grated. 'Fall in love with me?' His harsh laughter filled the enclosed space of the patio. 'Is that what you honestly think of me? That I am so weak-willed, so cowardly, that I am reduced to such stratagems?' Numbly Davina shook her head, trying to conceal her tears. 'So our good doctor has told you that he *believes* my paralysis to be caused by a traumatic shock—and it is only a belief; it cannot be proved. Has he also told you of the odds against that mental block being removed?'

'Yes.'

'I suggest you examine your own motives a little more closely before you delve into mine, Davina. For instance, what motivates a woman to stay with a man without love existing between them?'

What answer could she give? A love so strong that it overrode common sense and pride?

When she and Jamie emerged from the Palacio an hour later, Ruy was already seated in the driving seat of a sleek Mercedes coupé.

His mother would be using the chauffeur-driven car, he explained as Jamie begged to be allowed to sit in the front passenger seat, and this car had been especially adapted for him to drive, he added suavely when Davina suggested to Jamie that it might be best if he sat in the back.

'I wasn't doubting your driving ability,' Davina began defensively, but Ruy's raised eyebrows said that he did not believe her.

'No? Then in that case you won't mind sitting beside me yourself, will you? That way Jamie can sleep in the back if he gets tired.'

It was so obviously a sensible suggestion that Davina found herself sliding reluctantly on to the cream hide seat while Jamie climbed into the back.

The car smelled of expensive hide and the thin cigars Ruy sometimes smoked. There was a box of them in front of him, and he lit one as they waited for Rodriguez to finish loading the luggage. Davina had been surprised that the manservant was not to accompany them, but Ruy had explained that he would go straight to the *estancia*. Blue smoke from the cigarillo curled lazily upwards, the smell of the tobacco reminding her evocatively of that first meeting in Cordoba when he had bought her coffee and listened to her pouring out her story.

The boot was closed. The Condesa was waiting to wave them off. Ruy switched on the engine and they started to move forward, the car coming to an abrupt halt that threw her against the padded dashboard as Ruy stopped suddenly when they had gone no more than a few yards.

'Seat-belt,' he reminded her sharply, when she turned to him. 'That was a small sample of what can happen when a driver has to brake suddenly.'

She had been so concerned about Ruy and Jamie

that she had forgotten this simple safety precaution. Her finances at home did not run to such luxuries as a car, and she had got out of the habit of thinking of herself as a passenger.

Shakily she reached for the strap, pulling it across her body, as she tried to push the metal tag into the holder. The fitting was tight and although she exerted as much pressure as she could, it was not sufficient to drive the tag home.

'Let me.' Her hands were pushed unceremoniously out of the way as Ruy's lean brown fingers deftly manipulated the belt. His knuckles brushed accidentally across the soft curve of her breast—completely impersonally—but she withdrew immediately nonetheless, not wanting him to think she had deliberately fumbled with the belt to engineer the brief contact. For a moment his fingers seemed to tremble—probably because of the pressure he was having to exert, but when the belt was securely fastened and adjusted he merely glanced remotely at her before re-starting the engine.

Davina had never been to Marbella before. The business venture which Ruy had entered with Concepcion's father had been started more recently. They were financing the building of a small number of select villas on a holiday complex, Ruy told her in answer to her queries.

The powerful Mercedes made light work of the long miles, the air-conditioning mitigating the effect of the heat outside, just as the tinted windows kept out the harsh glare of the sunlight.

Riding in a car was still a novelty to Jamie and it was easy to keep him amused by encouraging him to count all the different coloured cars he saw, and after a few miles even Ruy joined in the game, making Jamie laugh with triumph when his father occasionally missed seeing a car, allowing him to add to his score. But even while making allowances for his youth Ruy in no way patronised the little boy, correcting him firmly but quietly when he made a mistake or when his exuberance led him to attempting to cheat.

'Soon we shall have to make arrangements about his schooling,' Ruy commented to Davina when Jamie was engrossed in the new game.

Cold fingers touched her heart. Of course she knew that Jamie was growing up and would soon be leaving babyhood behind and entering the world of men, but mother-like, she wanted to hold off the evil day as long as she could.

'What had you in mind?' she asked steadily, feeling that to betray her pain would only give Ruy a weapon to use against her. 'Boarding school?'

'Later, perhaps. There is an excellent school in Cordoba which he could attend. I do not believe in forcing children into a mould for which they are not fitted by nature, although in Jamie's case, as my son he will naturally, one day, have to step into my shoes. At the moment he is constantly among adults, and I think he would benefit from companions of his own age.'

Davina could find nothing to argue with in this statement. She turned her head and looked at Jamie's absorbed features.

'You love him a great deal.'

It was a statement rather than a question, but nevertheless she replied to it.

'Did you expect me not to? My own child?'

'And my child?' Ruy reminded her, his mouth compressing. 'Truly mother nature is wonderful, that she can cause a woman to love the child of a man for whom she feels nothing.'

They were driving along the valley of the Guadalquivir past rich cereal fields tended by peasants who worked tirelessly on the crops. This land had been under cultivation from the time of the Moors, and they had bequeathed to it the irrigation system which made it so rich and fertile. Groves of olive trees, their leaves silver-grey in the sunlight, bowed beneath the weight of their fruit. Jamie, to whom they were still new, demanded to know what the olives were used for, and patiently Ruy explained, 'To the Spaniard the olive is the symbol of prosperity. It was first brought to Spain by the Moors, along with peaches, pomegranates, medlars and many other fruits. At one time Seville had a reputation second to none for its learning and scholars. People came from all over Europe to consult its doctors and lawyers, so you have much to be proud of in your heritage, my son, and much to live up to.'

Jamie nodded his head in solemn agreement and then smiled sweetly and said vigorously, 'When I grow up I want to be just like my daddy. Can I learn to ride a real horse when we go to the *estancia*?'

Ruy glanced at Davina.

'I don't see why not. We shall find a small pony for you, and Rodriguez will teach you, as his father taught me.'

And as Ruy would have taught Jamie had it not been for his accident. Davina had to make a pretence of studying the landscape so that neither pair of male eyes would see her tears.

'Perhaps he'll teach me as well,' she said when she was sure that her voice would not betray her. 'I've always longed to be able to ride.'

Ruy made no comment. He was concentrating on overtaking a farm cart pulled by a small donkey wearing a straw hat threaded with faded pink roses, and Davina did not like to repeat the request. On their wedding night, after the culmination of their love-making, he had whispered huskily that there was much he would teach her, and that they would derive mutual pleasure from the lessons, but it was well known that men said many things they did not mean in the after-math of physical satisfaction. With painful clarity she remembered how he had held her close within the circle of his arms, kissing the tears of pleasure from her damp cheeks.

The Yacht Club had its own extensive grounds and had once been a private house. Balconied verandas overlooked the harbour, which was crammed with craft of all sizes and origins, the one thing they all had in common being their luxurious splendour.

His meeting should not take long, Ruy announced as he parked the car. The driver's seat had been removed to accommodate the wheelchair, and there was an electrical device to lift it from the car to the ground which retracted back inside the Mercedes once the manoeuvre was completed.

A steward appeared almost immediately to conduct Ruy to the room where he was to meet his business associates. They had an hour, he had told Davina, warning her that it would not be wise to stray too far, or stay overlong in the hot sun.

Bearing this in mind, she insisted on Jamie wearing his white linen sunhat. His chubby legs were already turning healthily brown. The Condesa had insisted on buying him some new clothes and as they set off hand in hand for the harbour, Davina was amused to hear a passerby comment loud enough for her to hear. 'Just look at that darling little boy! So Spanish!'

The quayside bustled with activity—people coming and going from the various craft; men with skin like leather and eyes fanned by a network of lines, dressed in jeans and tee-shirts; girls in brief shorts and tops. Everywhere except for the half dozen or so yachts which to Davina's uneducated eyes more resembled full-scale liners, the accent was on casual clothes, but Davina smiled to see two men dressed in navy pin-striped suits and carrying briefcases gingerly going on board one of the larger yachts.

'The boss's private secretaries,' the seaman standing by the gangway told Davina cheerfully with a wink. 'Keeps 'em busy, he does.'

The two men had looked very hot and uncomfortable. She wouldn't like to be at the beck and call of a rich boss, Davina thought. Jamie drew her attention to a speedboat circling the bay, a girl on water-skis behind it, wearing the briefest bikini Davina had ever seen in her life.

'I want to do that,' Jamie insisted, tugging on her hand, and when Davina told him that it was very, very hard, he replied cheerfully with the sublime confidence of the very young, 'I bet my daddy can do it. I bet he can do it a hundred times better than that lady!'

Davina squeezed his hand, too moved to speak. She had never seen Ruy water-skiing, but she knew that he could. Sebastian had told her that he had won a shield for it, and she knew that he was practically a championship swimmer. That pleasure at least had not been taken away from him.

Jamie insisted on having an ice-cream although,

knowing that they would shortly be having lunch, Davina prudently bought him a very small one.

An eye-catching outfit in a harbourside boutique drew her attention. It was a female version of the traditional male Spanish riding costume, and on impulse she went in and asked if she might try it on.

It fitted perfectly. She had lost a little weight since coming to Spain and the narrow black trousers emphasised her slender waist.

'It might have been made for you,' the girl told her. 'It is one of our most popular lines.' She wrinkled her nose despairingly. 'But you try telling a size sixteen tourist that it really isn't their style!'

By the time it was wrapped up and the bill paid Davina realised that they ought to be heading back to the Club. When she stepped outside into the bright sunshine a wave of dizziness swept over her. It was gone almost instantly. Hunger, she told herself firmly, grasping Jamie's hand, but as they got closer to the club, the noise and bright light of the quayside seemed to heighten in intensity to a point where it was making her feel physically ill.

Once inside the shady, cool foyer of the club, the nausea seemed to recede. A waiter came to conduct them to a table discreetly placed in a small alcove, permitting the maximum degree of privacy but still allowing an excellent view over the harbour and of the other diners.

Ruy was there already, talking to two other men, who smiled and bowed as she approached.

'Ah, there you are, darling!'

Was that really Ruy talking to her in a voice like warm brown velvet, reaching for her fingers to curl them round inside his own and brush them tenderly against his jaw? A tug on her arm brought her down towards him, the light kiss he placed against her lips making her stare at him in bemused wonder, her cheeks still flushing.

'My wife is still very English,' Ruy laughed. 'She believes that all gestures of affection should be conducted in privacy.'

Both men were eyeing Davina appreciatively. In fact although she was unaware of it her entrance had created quite a stir. Slim blonde girls with eyes the colour of amethysts, and a shyness that aroused the hunting instinct in the essentially male Spaniard, were a rare find in such modern times.

Sensing that something was expected of her, Davina leaned forward and brushed her lips against Ruy's skin. It felt hard and warm to touch, sending tiny electrical impulses through her own body, and making her long for the right to touch him as a lover.

The two men did not linger. Business must not be allowed to interfere with such a serious matter as eating lunch.

Davina let Ruy order for them. Their first course was tiny fried prawns in a delicious sauce accompanied by crisp rolls, but Davina could not finish it. The nagging headache which had begun outside the boutique seemed to have taken over her entire head. She made a pretence of picking at the salmon salad Ruy had ordered for them, hoping that Jamie's excited chatter would distract his attention away from her. Whether it was the sudden change of temperature from the harbour to the air-conditioned club, she did not know, but she suddenly felt chilled, almost to the point of shivering.

'What's the matter?' The coldly incisive words cut

through her pain. 'Was it the effort of pretending to be a loving wife that makes you look so pale? My associates have naturally heard about our marriage and expect to see us at least making a show of being happy together. They tell me that I am fortune to have such a loving wife. Fortunate!' He grimaced slightly. 'Would you agree with them, Davina? Would you say that I was "fortunate"—a man who cannot move without the assistance of others; a man whose wife turns from him in horror and disgust?'

You're wrong, she wanted to shout, but the words remained unsaid. Ruy was using her as a means of venting his wrath, that was all, but the cruelty in his probing expression as he added so softly that only she could hear, 'A wife whose body I can still arouse nonetheless, though . . .' deprived her of the ability to fight back.

Let him think of her what he wished, she decided dully, pushing away her meal barely touched, as long as he stopped tormenting her.

The road to the *estancia* went through the city of Ronda—traditional home of the bullfight, Ruy explained to Davina as they turned away from the coast and towards the Sierras, divided in two by the chasm that sliced it in half as neatly as a sword-slash.

Hairpin bends like a switchback track carried them up into the mountains, each swerving curve increasing Davina's nausea to the point where it was all she could do merely to remain upright in her seat. At one point she unwisely obeyed Jamie's excited command to 'look out of the window, Mummy!' and immediately wished she had not when she saw the drop below them, the remains of cars driven more carelessly than theirs rust-ing away in the gorge below.

'This is reputed to be one of the most dangerous roads in all Spain, and he wants to overtake me!' Ruy gritted at one point, glancing into his mirror. The shrill blare of a horn behind them confirmed his words, and as Davina glanced over her shoulder she saw a small scarlet sports car on their tail, its hood down, and four young people crammed into a space intended only for two.

'Crazy fools!' Ruy swore succinctly. 'Do they want to kill themselves! *Loco! Turistas!* They are a menace to other people's safety!'

A glance at the speedometer showed that they themselves were travelling at some speed, although the expensive engineering of the car nullified some of its effects, but the driver of the red sports car seemed determined to pass them, even though the road was busy and barely wide enough for two cars.

'*Cristo!*' Ruy swore at one point, when he was forced to brake and they could hear squealing tyres behind them. 'I should like to give those young fools a piece of my mind. Do they know how many people have lost their lives on this road, I wonder?'

They reached a point where the road started to climb steeply, and to Davina's relief the powerful Mercedes soon pulled away from the overloaded sports car.

'If I were not confined to this damned chair, I would have stopped and spoken to them,' Ruy said bitterly. '*Por Dios!* I could just see their faces had I done so—a cripple . . .'

His anger seemed to fill the car like a dense cloud, silencing Jamie and making Davina long for the ability to shrug aside the pain-filled sickness which seemed to keep coming and going in ever-strengthening waves.

She lifted a hand to her head, trying to ease the agonising throbbing, but even that movement was sufficient to make her shiver with the effort of suppressing her nausea.

'What's the matter? Are you car-sick?' Ruy demanded, lifting his eyes from the road to follow the betraying gesture.

Davina could only shake her head, even that small motion excruciatingly painful.

'I don't know.' Her voice was merely a thread of sound. 'My head aches. I feel sick, and dizzy . . . I feel so cold . . .'

'Heatstroke! Did you not have the sense to cover your head when you were out this morning?'

Davina was beyond replying. She merely wanted to curl up and die, but rather than admit that Ruy was right she sat bolt upright in her seat and stared out of the car window.

They were driving through mountains of rust red sandstone, sprinkled with moss and alpine flowers. She remembered reading somewhere once that the Garrison at Gibraltar used to spend the dog days of summer at Ronda where the air was cooler.

Beneath them lay the plain and the coast, but mindful of her nausea Davina refused to look back. Ronda itself was all narrow, winding streets and ancient buildings. Ruy pointed out to her the bridge across the chasm of red sandstone from which its designer had fallen to his death, dizzied by the depth of the gorge.

The *estancia* lay beyond the town and had at one time served as a summer residence for the family. It was Ruy who had built up their herd of bulls, all carefully bred for the arena. Bulls came in two classes, he explained to Jamie as they drew nearer the *estancia*; either young bulls three to four years old or older ones of four to five which were used in the *corrida* proper. The bulls had to be bred to an extremely exacting standard. Their weight must fall within certain limits; their age must be correct, and most important of all, they must be brave. 'A cowardly bull disgraces a brave *torero*, just as a cowardly man disgraces a brave bull,' he told a round-eyed Jamie, who was listening with awe.

A narrow road with cattle grids across it led to the *estancia*. Davina could see no sign of the bulls as they drove past flat paddocks. This was because during the heat of the summer the animals were kept where there was most water, Ruy told her. Thousands of pounds were invested in these animals and nothing could afford to be left to chance.

'It seems pointless, when they are going to die anyway,' Davina commented. She had never witnessed a *corrida*, although Ruy had once told her that it was not for the spectacle of a blood sport that his country-men flocked to the bullfight; it was something that went far deeper than that; left over from the days when man worshipped the goddess of fertility, and the male for-tunate enough to be chosen as her mate reigned as king for a year before being sacrificed for continued pros-perity. Gradually as cultures evolved the bull had come to take the place of man, as depicted in the Minoan culture, and it was from this that the bullfight had evolved. To the Spaniard the experience was an en-nobling and uplifting one—almost religious, and the death of a good bull was mourned almost as much as the death of a good matador.

At last they reached the hacienda. It was a double-storey house with a long low frontage and a delicate veranda running its full length, wrought iron balconies ornamenting the upper windows, the entire façade smothered in the purple flowers of the bougainvillea through which the delicate white-painted tracery of the wrought iron gleamed softly in the late afternoon sun.

As the dust from the car tyres settled doors opened and Rodriguez, accompanied by a small, plump woman with eyes like raisins, her hair in a neat bun, came hurrying out to meet them.

Jamie was lifted from the car and snatched to an ample bosom, a torrent of excited Spanish engulfing them as Davina struggled to extricate herself from her seat. Where she had been cold she was now hot; her dress was sticking damply to her back, perspiration beading her forehead. Her body ached with fatigue and she longed to lie down somewhere quiet and cool.

'Dolores says that Jamie is a true Silvadores,' Ruy told her wryly as the Spanish woman continued to hug the little boy. 'She has seven children of her own, three of whom are living here on the *estancia* with their parents, so Jamie will not lack company. Between them Dolores and her husband, who is my manager, have been running the *estancia* since my father died. They look upon it as their home, and Dolores will have gone to a great deal of trouble to ensure our comfort.'

What was he trying to suggest? That she might find the hacienda wanting in some way? As she followed Dolores into a large, comfortably furnished *sala*, its shutters closed against the bright sunlight, Davina could not imagine why he should think so.

It was true that the hacienda lacked the elegance of the Palacio, but the house had a comfortable, family air, which appealed to her instantly. Here small children would be able to run about and touch to their

hearts' content. The furniture was no less well cared
for than that in the Palacio, but somehow it was less
intimidating. Sturdy, cushion-filled settees and chairs
invited one to sit on them; brightly woven carpets
overlaid the coolly tiled floors. There was a jug of
flowers on the coffee table, and along one wall ran
shelves which housed books and magazines that seemed
to relate to farm management. The room could have
been that of a comfortably off farmer rather than a
Spanish grandee, and Davina was not ashamed to
admit that she liked its ambience; the smell of leather
and beeswax mingling with the hot, dusty scent of the
land.

'I have given you the bedroom of the *patrón*,' the
woman explained as she led Davina up the gracefully
curved stairs to the upper storey. Ruy had already
warned her that here at the *estancia* they dispensed
with titles. To these people he was simply 'the *patrón*'.
The title had a patriarchal air which suited him.
Davina found herself imagining him as an old man
surrounded by his family. Her heart gave a small
thump; she must not give way to such foolish visions.

The bedroom she was shown was large. Floral wallpaper adorned the walls, the theme continued in the
curtains and bedspread. The bed was a fourposter, the
furniture Spanish provincial. Off the bedroom was a
bathroom and small dressing room, both showing signs
of having been recently modernised. The bathroom
fittings reflected the same country style as the bedroom, the white porcelain painted with flowers and
leaves.

'You like?' Dolores beamed up at her. 'It is all new
since the *patrón* marries, for his *novia* . . . *si* . . .'

Davina's stomach plummeted downwards and she

stared round the room with new eyes. All this had been done for Carmelita. She touched the pastel wallpaper tentatively. Somehow the room did not strike her as suitable for the other girl's vibrant personality. She, on the other hand, loved it. The moment she walked in the room she had felt her taut muscles start to relax. The sheets smelled of crushed lavender, and the scent hung evocatively on the air. Lavender. She smiled to herself. Such an English scent! Surely carnation or something equally exotic would have been more suitable for Carmelita?

Rodrigues came upstairs with the luggage. Both her cases and Ruy's were placed on the floor, Davina noticed, remembering her vow that on their removal to the *estancia* she would tell Ruy that she wanted her own room.

'The *pequeño* grows anxious for his dinner,' Rodrigues told Dolores.

'He has been ill,' Davina found herself confiding to the other woman—a mother herself, after all. 'The damp climate . . .'

'But here he will grow tall and strong, you will see,' Dolores beamed.

The sickness Davina had experienced on the journey returned over dinner. Dolores had prepared a dish of crisply fried chicken served on a bed of peppers and sweetcorn. Jamie tucked into it with every evidence of enjoyment. Apart from during his illness he had never been a fussy eater, and Davina was relieved to see that he seemed to be adapting to a changed diet without too much trouble. She herself could barely force down a mouthful. They were eating early because Ruy wanted to spend the evening in discussion with the estate manager.

'The bedroom is to your satisfaction?' he enquired as he poured her a glass of wine.

'It's very attractive.' Her voice sounded listless. 'Dolores told me it has been decorated quite recently—for your *novia*, she told me.' It was impossible to prevent the hint of bitterness from creeping into the words. 'I shouldn't have thought it in accord with Carmelita's personality.'

To her amazement Ruy's jaw clenched in anger, a pulse beating warningly beneath the skin as he drank his wine before saying curtly, 'That room was not decorated for Carmelita. It was decorated for my wife—for you. I arranged for it to be done while you were carrying Jamie. I had thought after his birth that we might spend more time out here. Its atmosphere is more conducive to family life than the Palacio's.'

Davina didn't know what to say. The thought of Ruy going to all this trouble on her behalf stunned her. She remembered the lavender perfumed sheets, and the furnishings which now that she thought about them closely resembled those to be found in an English country house. No wonder she had had such a nostalgic sense of coming home!

'Ruy, I just don't know what to say . . .' she began weakly, but he brushed aside her words, shrugging as though he had grown bored with the matter.

'It no longer matters,' he drawled, confirming his actions. 'The room was prepared in vastly different circumstances from those we now find ourselves in.'

What he meant was that now he no longer needed to ease his conscience by providing her with pleasant surroundings as compensation for not being able to give her his love.

He left the table before she could tell him that she

did not want to share a room with him. With Jamie to be bathed and put to bed, his excited questions all answered, and the pain in her temples to contend with, Davina herself was on the point of crawling into the comfort of the cool sheets before she remembered that Ruy was still downstairs and she had not been able to speak to him.

She bit her lip and glanced to the other side of the bed where his robe had been carefully laid out. She could scarcely demand that he find another bed tonight.

She could talk to him tomorrow, she decided sleepily, reaching out to switch off the lamp. She had gone very cold again, the cool sheets now felt like an Arctic wasteland, and her body longed treacherously for the warmth of Ruy against her.

CHAPTER EIGHT

DAVINA woke up feeling cold, taking several minutes to remember where she was. Her head ached and there was a sour taste in her mouth. She reached for the bedside lamp and then realised that Ruy was asleep at the other side of the bed. Rather than risk waking him she pushed back the sheets and tiptoed towards the bathroom.

Her head hurt, and her face looked flushed. Ruy was right, she reflected as she studied her reflection. She ought to have worn a hat when she was out in the sun. She had forgotten how strong it could be. Cleaning her teeth dispelled the unpleasant taste in her mouth. She had some aspirins in her handbag and she resolved to take a couple before going back to bed.

The windows to the balcony stood open, allowing the hot night scents to drift into the bedroom. Davina knew that the temperature had not suddenly dropped ten degrees, but as she crossed to the bed the breeze from the window brought out tiny bumps of gooseflesh on her arms—the aftermath of too much sun. Below the windows the darkness was full of the sound of crickets, petals from a jacaranda carpeting the balcony floor.

As she slid back into bed Ruy moved and muttered something under his breath in Spanish, his features for once relaxed. Asleep, he looked more like the man she had married. A sudden fit of shivering seized her, making her teeth chatter.

'*Amada . . .*'

Ruy didn't open his eyes, but his arm came round her, pulling her against the warmth of his body, the heat from his skin bringing hers tinglingly alive, his warm breath fanning across her temple.

Chiding herself for giving in to the demand of her senses so easily, Davina allowed herself to luxuriate in his proximity. His action had been no more than a simple reflex, she warned herself; and meant nothing, except perhaps that he was dreaming that he held Carmelita in his arms. The thought made her move slightly away from him, but his arm tightened possessively, dragging her against him, his lips teasing tender kisses against the vulnerable skin of her throat and shoulders.

'Ruy . . .'

She tried to push him away, but his arm only hardened, his husky, '*Querida?*' turning her bones to water. She looked at him and saw that his eyes were still closed even though his fingertips were making a delicate exploration of her body.

She was a fool, she told herself when Ruy pushed aside the thin cotton of her nightdress and buried his head in the shadowed hollow between her breasts, holding her to him as though he never wanted to let her go. This time his touch held tenderness—worship almost, the soft Spanish lovewords whispering past his lips, punctuated by seductive kisses, weakening her shaky resolve. It would be so easy to respond to him, to encourage him even, but she was convinced that he was not aware who she was. His lovemaking held a quality she remembered from their honeymoon; sensual and lazy, that of a man who touches for the tactile pleasure of doing so. There was no sense of urgency, no driven furious anger, and never once did his eyes open as he stroked and caressed her body into melting surrender, murmuring to her in Spanish, husky words of passion intermingled with the moist warmth of his mouth as it touched her body in tender worship.

'*Amada . . .*'

Davina heard him whisper it on a satisfied sigh as his lips brushed hers, and he begged her to tell him of her love.

Tears stung her eyes. How gladly she would have complied, if she thought for one moment that he might have wanted it. But the soft words and sweet kisses falling from his lips were not for her.

She held her breath and prayed that he would not wake up, and soon the even rise and fall of his breathing told her that her prayers had been granted, although when she tried to move away from him to her own side of the bed he refused to let her go, and she slept, as she had dreamed of doing for so long, clasped in the arms of the man she loved, his heart beating beneath her cheek, her palms spread against the satin warmth of his skin.

'Kiss me, *amada* . . .' The sleep-drugged words penetrated, and Davina's eyelids fluttered open. She was lying in Ruy's arms, his lips feathering light kisses along her jawbone.

'Ruy?'

'*Dios*, I want you!'

She could feel his heart thudding beneath her palms, his face pale in the morning light. He bent his head, parting her lips with the mastery she remembered, coaxing her mouth to give up its sweetness. Beneath her hands his heartbeat accelerated, his body tautening with the desire that throbbed pulsating through him, making plain his need. Her own body was half crushed beneath his superior weight, the powerful muscles of his thighs contracting in sudden urgency as his hands slid her nightgown from her shoulders, his lips plundering the creamy curves bared to his burning gaze, and playing on her body like a master drawing a response from a carefully tuned violin.

'Ruy . . .' Her protest was lost beneath the warm pressure of his mouth, draining her of the will to resist, his fingers tangling in her hair as he held her head pinioned to allow his lips to rove freely where they wished.

She managed to drag her lips away for long enough to whisper his name again. His body crushing her to the bed, his hands either side of her face on the pillow, he raised himself slightly to stare down into her pale face.

'You are my wife, Davina,' he said broodingly, 'and you have brought home to me the fact that I am a man. Sharing a bedroom with you has reminded me of all that I have been missing. Your skin is like silk beneath my hands and you tremble at my slightest touch like a shy virgin who has never known a man. You taste of roses and honey and your hair is the colour of moonbeams. A man would have to be made of stone to resist your beauty, and I am only flesh and blood. See,' he said softly, taking her hand and placing it against his body. 'Can you not feel what you do to me?'

'Ruy, this is madness!' Davina protested, more shaken than she wanted him to see by his words. He thought her beautiful! He desired her, but desire was not love.

'Of a certainty,' he agreed with a mocking smile, 'but it is a madness that mortals need to keep them sane. Why deny me, Davina, when you have permitted so many others? I am your husband . . .'

'And because of that I'm supposed to allow you to treat me like . . . like a harem slave?' Davina demanded bitterly. 'I thought better of you, Ruy. I didn't think you would take a woman without love, purely to satisfy a sexual appetite.'

'Neither did I, but needs must when the devil drives, as he is driving me.'

He lowered his head and knowing that he wouldn't be swayed, Davina sought wildly for time. This wasn't how she wanted him to make love to her, as a substitute for Carmelita.

'Think . . .' she begged him despairingly. 'We'll only end up hating each other—hating ourselves . . .'

'Perhaps.' The word grazed her skin like a kiss. 'But in the meantime we would have known a shared sweetness; an oblivion that brings its own recompense. Will you not taste that oblivion with me, sweet Davina?'

As his mouth closed over hers Davina fought its insistent pressure like a drowning man fighting water. Beneath his hands her body turned to pure flame, betraying her even while she resisted.

'Davina.' Her name was a thick plea on Ruy's tongue, overturning all her determination, like a spring tide crashing through a sea wall, carrying her back with it to a place where nothing mattered but the feel of Ruy's skin beneath her hands, the harsh warmth of his mouth as he filled her senses to the exclusion of everything but the driving need in the lower half of her body, prompting her to arch imploringly beneath the heated thrust of the thighs imprisoning her, Ruy's

name a soft moan of desire-laden protest as his lips left
the vulnerable hollows behind her ears to torment the
throbbing pulses of her neck and lower still, while her
own lips fastened on the tanned column of his throat,
her teeth biting sensually into the sunwarmed skin.

'*Dios* . . . *querida*, but I want you!'

The tormented groan seemed to shiver right through
her, finding all her most vulnerable corners, making
her flesh quiver with a yearning need which could only
find appeasement in Ruy's complete possession.

'Ruy . . .' All her longing for him was in that one
word and he lifted his head to survey her with eyes
black as night and burning with desire.

'Ah, now you do not talk of hating one another, do
you, *querida*? Do you feel as I do? Does your body
long to be united with mine, no longer separate, but a
part of one enticingly perfect whole? Does your need
for fulfilment overcome all your moral scruples? Do
you want me as I want you?'

'Yes.' The shamed whisper could not be held back.

'So . . .'

He turned abruptly as someone knocked on the bedroom door, and then frowned as he glanced at his watch
on the bedside table.

'*Dios!*' he swore softly. 'I had forgotten. I asked
Rodriguez to wake me early so that I could go down to
the bull pens. What shall I do, *amada*? Send him
away?'

Davina flushed at the openly sensual tone.

Those few seconds' respite had given her the chance
to allow common sense to reassert itself, and she shook
her head, moving away from Ruy's constraining
hands.

'Ah,' he mocked softly, 'I had forgotten that prim

English streak. You surprise me, *querida*. A woman of your experience should not be embarrassed because it is known that your husband would rather lie in bed in the mornings and make love to you than visit his livestock.'

'Lovemaking without love,' Davina said tiredly.

'So! But very enjoyable nonetheless,' Ruy said cruelly. 'Do not deny it. One only has to look in the mirror. Your face is that of a woman who has recently been aroused.'

'Desire is not enough—at least not for me, Ruy.'

All at once his face seemed to close up and grow cold.

'I think you are deceiving yourself, *querida*,' he said harshly. 'But now is perhaps not the time to prove the truth of my statement.' He called out something in Spanish to Rodriguez, and Davina turned away from him in despair. How quickly she had plummeted from the heights to the depths! It was pointless telling herself that he wanted her physically; to allow him to possess her in such circumstances would be an act of insanity which would eventually destroy them both.

'You were going to allow me to make love to you, Davina,' Ruy said evenly from behind her, 'however much you try to deny it. Was it only desire?'

Her cheeks burned as she realised how close he had come to stumbling upon the truth. No matter what happened he must not guess that she still loved him.

'Yes,' she lied bravely. 'And besides, I've already told you—I don't think it's good for Jamie to be an only one.'

'Damn you, Davina!' Ruy ground viciously in the silence that followed. 'Damn you to hell!'

'I'm sorry I'm late, Dolores,' Davina apologised as she sat down at the table. 'I'm afraid I . . . overslept . . .'

For the life of her she could not prevent the colour running up betrayingly under her skin. She was quite sure that the entire household knew exactly why she was late for breakfast—and she shot Ruy a bitter look as Dolores beamed cheerfully and chuckled, '*De nada* . . . It is the second honeymoon, *sí*?'

She laughed again, while Jamie looked uncertainly from Davina to Ruy as though he sensed the bitter undercurrents between them.

'Have you thanked Dolores for making you such a lovely breakfast?' Davina asked him to distract his attention.

'*Gracias*, Dolores,' the little boy said solemnly. He had already picked up quite a few words of Spanish and unlike Davina was not shy of showing off his new achievement.

'*De nada, pequeño,*' Dolores assured him. 'It is a pity your *madre* does not eat more, *no*? But then love steals away the appetite, is this not so?'

Davina dropped the roll she had been crumbling absently as though it were red hot, not daring to look at Ruy. She could hardly believe that the calmly remote man sitting next to her was the same one who had whispered such tender words of love such a short time ago.

Half asleep and still dreaming of Carmelita, Davina reminded herself. No wonder his manner was so icily distant now! He obviously wanted to leave her in no doubt about his lack of feeling for her.

'Today I'm going to learn to ride,' Jamie confided importantly as he drank his orange juice. 'Rodriguez has already promised that I might. Papa is going to take me to see the bulls afterwards. They're very big and I'm not to go near them on my own.'

Davina glanced at Ruy for confirmation that he did actually intend to take the little boy down to the bull-pens, but he was engrossed in his mail, reading a long letter written on lavender-coloured paper, and scented with carnation—a letter quite obviously from a woman.

'Will you come with us when we go down to the stables?' Jamie asked her.

'Your mother will not want to risk getting her clothes dirty, I am sure,' Ruy answered for her, briefly lifting his head to glance warningly at her.

'Oh, I can change into my jeans quickly enough,' Davina replied, pinning on a false smile. Ruy had made it quite obvious that he didn't want her to accompany them, but she was not going to be deprived of her son's company simply because his father could not bear the sight of her.

Ten minutes later the three of them were making their way down to the stables, Jamie's excited chatter covering the silence between his parents.

They were within easy distance of the house, but remembering the effects of being out in the hot sunshine the previous day, Davina had taken the precaution of wearing a large-brimmed sun hat to protect herself from the strong rays. Likewise Jamie was wearing his hat, but Ruy was bareheaded, the sun turning his dark hair blue-black as it emphasised the tanned column of his throat and the fine sprinkling of dark body hair beneath the thin white silk shirt.

There were half a dozen loose boxes, but only three of them were occupied. The animals in the first two were used for work on the *estancia*, so Ruy told Jamie, explaining that this had two advantages. Firstly the horse could go where it was impossible to take a Land Rover, however stoutly constructed, and secondly it prepared the bull for the sight and smell of horses in the bullring. He went on to explain to a wide-eyed Jamie that there was a tradition connected with the bullfight, dating back to the days when this had been conducted not on foot, but on horseback, and that although nowadays matadors fought on foot at every bullfight there was still an exhibition of the traditional Andalusian horses and their riders, performing manoeuvres which in their way were as spectacular as those of the Lipizzaner stallions of the Spanish Riding School in Vienna, whose forebears had been pure bred Andalusian horses.

Davina had only witnessed it once, at her one and only bullfight, but the memory of the white horses and their darkly handsome riders in their traditional costumes had stayed with her. Such riding was now the sport of rich young men, Ruy had told her, because they alone could afford the costly horses. He himself had owned an Andalusian stallion, named Cadiz, and it had been this horse which had carried Davina to the Fair in Seville.

She mentioned him to Ruy, wondering at the tiny warning shake of his head Rodriguez directed towards her.

'A highly bred stallion is not an animal for a man who is a cripple,' Ruy told her harshly. 'Cadiz only owned me as master as long as I had his respect.'

For one horrified moment Davina had wild visions of Ruy ordering the animal to be destroyed, as she had heard of Caliphs doing in those long-ago days when the Moors brought their Arab steeds to Spain, but to her relief, Ruy told her that Cadiz was now lodged at a stud farm owned by a friend of his.

'Where he longs for the green pastures of his home,' Rodriguez commented, with the first sign of dis-approval Davina had ever heard him express.

'Cadiz, like the rest of us, must learn that life cannot always be just as we would wish it,' Ruy said harshly. 'In many ways I am a fool to keep him. I should have sold him. I shall certainly never ride him again.'

'Where's my pony?' Jamie demanded plaintively, bringing a welcome interruption to the conversation. Davina could imagine what anguish it must have caused Ruy to part with his horse. She remembered how on that one occasion when Ruy had held her up in front of him, horse and man had seemed to move with one mind, both supreme in their own individual ways.

'See, *pequeño*, here is your pony,' Rodriguez told Jamie, lifting him up so that he could see the soft muzzle just peeping over the top of the box.

Davina, who had been watching them, chanced to glance across at Ruy and surprised such a look of aching longing on his face that she looked away almost immediately, shaken by the feeling that she had just witnessed a man with all his barriers down and intruded upon an essentially private moment.

'What is the matter?' Ruy demanded of her, seeing the look. 'Am I not allowed to have emotions, to wish that I were the one to hold my son up to his first mount, to feel his body in my arms and know the wonder of touching a part of my own flesh?'

'I didn't think you cared,' was all Davina could find to say. 'He's nearly four years old, and never once . . .'

'Because I knew I could not look at him and then

turn my back on him,' Ruy said fiercely. 'A clean cut and a quick one is always far preferable to an aching wound that festers and eventually kills.'

What was he trying to say? That he had wanted Jamie? Then why had he never made any attempt to see him? Even though they might have remained estranged there had been nothing to prevent Ruy from building up a relationship with his son. Unless, of course, Carmelita had demanded that he did not do so.

'You told me you couldn't even be sure that he was yours,' Davina reminded him, touching a wound which still had the power to hurt.

'And so I told myself. It made it easier for me to keep to my decision, but to look at him is to know his fathering, is this not so?'

'Look at me, Papa!' Jamie crowed triumphantly from the back of the placid pony. 'I'm riding!'

Rodriguez was walking him quietly round the yard, keeping within an easy arm's distance in case of any mishaps, but Jamie seemed to have no sense of fear, his face alight with pleasure as he held on to the reins.

Davina felt her heart swell and lift as she looked at her son, and tried to quell the bitter ache Ruy's words had aroused. All this time she had thought that Ruy was ignoring Jamie's existence simply because he had no interest in the little boy—because Jamie had not been born to the woman he really loved—and yet now Ruy was trying to tell her that his indifference had sprung from the belief that Jamie might not have been his son.

'His paternity, yes,' she agreed proudly, hoping that Ruy wouldn't see the tears in his eyes, 'but it takes more than mere conception to be a father.'

She fled before Ruy could answer, unable to bear

the sharp scrutiny of eyes which she felt must surely probe the secret lying deep in her heart.

Davina was in her room when she heard a car draw up outside the house. Ruy was still down at the stable yard, and she was hurriedly pulling on the skirt she had removed before lying down on the bed when Dolores knocked on the door.

When Davina opened it the first thing she noticed was the air of suppressed excitement about the other woman.

'It is Señor Carlos,' she told Davina breathlessly. 'He has come to see the bulls. It is many, many months since he was last here. He is *muy hombre, sí*?'

Davina laughed. Even Dolores was not proof against Carlos' charm.

'Once Señor Carlos spend much time here,' Dolores told her as she waited for Davina to finish brushing her hair, 'but that was before the Conde's accident.'

'Condesa!'

The warm pressure of Carlos' lips against her fingers belied the formality of his greeting, and Davina had to fight to prevent herself from snatching her hand back in adolescent confusion.

From the twinkle in Carlos' eyes she suspected that he was by no means unaware of her reaction, and soft colour washed over her cheeks.

'Please bring us some *fino* and almond biscuits, Dolores,' she requested, trying to appear calm. 'Ruy is down at the stables,' she added to Carlos. 'Jamie is having his first riding lesson and . . .'

'Naturally the proud papa wishes to be there,' Carlos finished for her. 'As I would myself had I such a fine son, although I confess my loyalties would be divided.'

When Davina looked confused, he smiled and leaned forward so that she could see the thick darkness of his eyelashes brushing the warm olive of his skin. 'With such a beautiful wife as yourself, *querida*, I should want to spend every minute with you, and yet the bond between father and son is also very precious. Ruy is an extremely lucky man.'

Dolores returned with the sherry and small almond biscuits before Davina could remonstrate with Carlos for flirting with her. They were sitting on the patio sipping the fine dry liquid when Davina heard the soft hiss of the wheelchair and Jamie came running towards her.

'So this is your son, Ruy,' Carlos said carelessly when Ruy was within earshot. 'He is a fine boy.'

'Carlos. What brings you here?'

The question was terse and for the life of her Davina could not prevent her eyes from sliding to Carlos' face to see how he took Ruy's less than enthusiastic welcome.

He affected not to notice it, shrugging lightly.

'I am to fight in the ring at Ronda this week and so I thought I would come and see your bulls—and of course your beautiful wife. Also, I was hoping I might be able to beg a bed overnight.'

'I have prepared Señor Carlos' favourite paella,' Dolores announced, arriving with a glass of milk for Jamie. 'It is good that he visits us again, *si*?'

'I am sure my wife agrees with you, Dolores,' Ruy said heavily, turning to his manservant. 'Rodriguez, I wish to go to my room—help me, will you? Dolores will prepare a room for you,' he added.

Davina was on her feet automatically, reaching for the chair, but to her chagrin Ruy pushed her away roughly.

'You must forgive Ruy,' she said huskily when she and Carlos were alone. 'He finds it hard to accept the help of others . . .'

'And so he takes pleasure in humiliating you?' Carlos asked softly. 'You are very loyal, *pequeña*. Ruy is one of my oldest friends, but for the way he behaved towards you just now I could willingly have knocked him to the floor. Why do you endure it?'

'Because I love him,' Davina admitted jerkily. 'But it's no use—he doesn't love me.'

'No?' Carlos asked softly. 'I know jealousy when I see it, *querida*.'

'If Ruy is jealous it's only because he considers me to be his possession—there can be no other reason—you see, I know who he does love.'

The moment the words were uttered Davina wished them unsaid, but it was too late to recall them, and Carlos was watching her with compassionate understanding.

'So . . . Who is this woman?'

'Carmelita,' Davina said huskily. 'He married me only to spite her.' She couldn't think why she was confiding in Carlos like this. Perhaps it had something to do with the fact that she could no longer tolerate the burden of her thoughts alone.

'If he does, then he is a fool,' Carlos said savagely. 'To put a woman like that above you! I cannot believe it. I know Carmelita well. The man she has married was the fiancé of Concepcion—nothing had been formalised, but it was understood that there would be a marriage. He is extremely wealthy and I am convinced that it was purely because of his wealth that Carmelita seduced him away from my poor cousin, who, although she tries to hide it from us, has suffered badly over the

affair. In Spain it is still considered the utmost humiliation for a girl to be jilted. Ruy and I quarrelled over
it. Knowing him to be close to Carmelita, I begged
him to intercede with her on Concepcion's behalf, but
he refused.'

'Because he could not bear to deny her anything she
wanted,' Davina said bitterly. 'Oh, it's useless. I wish
I had never returned to Spain—never . . .'

Without any warning tears filled her eyes. She tried
to dash them away, but not before Carlos had seen
them.

'Poor *pequeña*,' he said softly. 'You must teach that
husband of yours that if he neglects you there are other
men who will not be so backward—myself included.'
He captured her fingers, raising them to his lips and
kissing them slowly. 'You are very beautiful, little
Davina, and if you were not so much in love with your
husband I would attempt to steal you away from him.
As it is . . .' His fingers tightened suddenly and before
Davina could divine his purpose his head bent swiftly,
capturing her lips in a brief kiss. Before he released
her he whispered softly against her ear, 'Ruy has just
come in and is watching us. I do not think he likes
what we are doing, *pequeña*.'

That was the understatement of the year, Davina
reflected as Carlos set her free and she turned round
slowly to see Ruy seated in his wheelchair by the door,
his face a frozen mask of rage.

At once she was on her feet, hurrying across to
him, but as she reached the wheelchair, he swung it
round abruptly, swearing as it collided with the
door.

'Ruy . . .' her protest went unheard as he pulled
himself upwards and with a superhuman effort held

himself erect before Rodriguez suddenly emerged on to the patio, his gasp of dismay coinciding with a sudden loss of balance as Ruy started to collapse.

Davina was nearest. Her arms went out to catch him, but he thrust her away with such violent force that the rough stonework of the wall grazed her arm, and it was Rodriguez who supported him back to the chair and wheeled him into the house.

'Oh, Carlos, how could you do that?' Davina protested when they were alone.

'How could I not?' Carlos said disarmingly. 'I like kissing lovely girls, and besides, I wanted to put a theory to the test. Ruy is not as indifferent to you as you believe, I am sure of it. All he needs is to be made a little jealous—to be forced to realise what you mean to him. You are, after all, his wife, and to a Spaniard marriage is sacred . . .'

When Davina shook her head, Carlos pressed, 'But did you not see the way in which he pulled himself to his feet? A man who is supposedly crippled? Does that not tell you something?'

It did! Davina remembered what Dr Gonzales had told her. Because he was furiously angry with her Ruy had got to his feet. Although she knew quite well that he did not care in the slightest about her, Davina could see how it would hurt his pride if he thought she was attracted to another man. But would it hurt it enough to make him overcome the mental block and walk? How angry did she have to make him to achieve that?

'I have an idea,' Carlos was saying. 'We shall conduct a little flirtation, you and I, and we shall see who is right. I am convinced that Ruy does care for you.'

Nothing Davina could say would sway him. All through dinner Carlos insisted on paying her the most lavish compliments and she could feel Ruy's eyes upon her. When the meal was over she excused herself, saying that she was tired. Carlos insisted on kissing her hand in the same intimate fashion as before. Davina dared not even look at Ruy.

As she prepared for bed she thought of what Carlos had said about Carmelita—how Ruy must love her—and her throat ached with suppressed tears. Carlos was so sure that Ruy cared for her, but she knew better, and yet for a moment he had been so furious with her that he had actually stood up without any help ... If only she could give him back the ability to walk, but how?

CHAPTER NINE

'THESE are the bulls used in the *novillada*,' Carlos was explaining to Davina as they inspected the bullpens together, 'and these larger animals the ones used in the *corrida* proper. There is no difference in the length or style of the bullfight, it is merely that in the *novillada*, we use the young bulls and junior matadors. Ruy himself once entered the ring as a *rejoneador*—that is one who fights the bulls on horseback. It is very skilled— very difficult.'

It was his first reference to Ruy since Davina had joined him at the breakfast table, and Davina was glad that he had not pressed her concerning Ruy's reaction to his 'flirtation'. She knew that Carlos meant to be kind and that it was possible to fan a spark into a conflagration, but first one needed the spark, and Ruy felt nothing for her.

'*Si*, Ruy and Cadiz worked well together in the ring. You will see what I mean this afternoon in Ronda, although the *rejoneadores* you will see there before the fight proper come nowhere near equalling him.'

'Why did he give it up?' Davina asked absently, shuddering a little as she studied the hard, solid-packed, muscled bodies of the bulls grazing beyond the electric fence—a necessary precaution, Carlos had told her, for an excitable bull was not above charging and destroying a fence if the mood so took him.

He shrugged. 'I once asked him, he said he preferred growing things to killing them, but that as such a

153

remark to a Spaniard comes close to heresy he did not wish it to be made public. In those days we were close friends and I understood his meaning. Between bull and matador exists a close communion, each knows he wins his life at the price of the other's, which is why in a good bullfight each feels respect for the other. I have never yet taken the life of a good bull without regret.'

Davina studied the bulls with a fast beating heart, feeling the primeval fear beat up inside her as the sunlight grazed the tips of the wickedly lethal horns, and she had a vivid impression of how it must have felt to be a Minoan bull-leaper and forced to grasp those horns and vault between them on to the bull's broad back. It made modern athletics, for all its rigorous training, seem tame in comparison, and she couldn't forget that it had been one of these animals who had gored and injured Ruy. As they watched, Dolores' husband and two young men on horses started to separate the bulls driving some towards them.

'Keep still,' Carlos warned her, even though they had the electric fence safely in front of them. 'A sudden quick movement is all it takes to distract their eye, I should hate to be obliged to demonstrate my skill with my bare hands and without my *trajes de luces*.' His droll comment made Davina laugh, as it had been intended to do, but fear still shivered through her. The bulls must cross the open courtyard before being penned to await transportation, and she made no demur when Carlos touched her arm and suggested that they leave.

'You were thinking of Ruy, were you not?' he said gently, as they walked back to the house.

Davina admitted it. 'Doesn't it frighten you?'

'Because his fate could so easily be mine?' Carlos

mused. 'One thinks of it, of course, but is that not half
of the appeal as it is always for those who engage in
danger; the thrill of the close breath of death; to feel
the dark angel's wings beating so close that one can
feel the draught, and then the exhilaration of knowing
one has cheated it—yet again. But to see Ruy as he is
is a sobering experience. I remember him when we
were at the university together in Seville. Such an
hombre . . . always the pretty girls!' He shrugged and
smiled reminiscently. 'It is different, of course, here
from England, but young people have their ways of
getting to know one another. Balconies are not always
inaccessible; our nights are warm and made for love,
and the moonlight a conspirator. But he was always,
behind his smile, serious. The weight of his responsibilities, you understand . . . He will be able to
spare Jamie much of those. His own father died when
he was fifteen and he was thrust into manhood while
still a boy. When I heard that he had married an
English girl with the shyness of a flower before it un-
furls and hair the colour of pale sand in the moonlight,
I was glad for him. For all his apparent self-sufficiency
he is a man who needs love more than any other. For
Ruy mere sexual satisfaction would not be enough.
Their feelings run deep, those of our countrymen who
have the blood of the Moro running through their
veins.'

Davina acknowledged that Carlos was probably
right, and her heart ached afresh to know that she
would never be the one to provide the love Ruy so
badly needed.

When they reached the courtyard Davina could hear
Jamie's voice raised in excitement.

'Look what Papa has given me!' he cried to Davina

when he saw her. On a chair was a beautiful handmade leather saddle of bright red to match the bridle Rodriguez had given him the previous day. Chased in silver and small enough for a very little boy, it had obviously been made especially for him. To his son Ruy could be generous, Davina admitted, giving him both love and care, but to her he showed another side of his nature, as he had done last night when she had tried to help him. She doubted that she would ever be able to forget the savage hatred in his eyes when he had pushed her away so violently.

'You must take care of the saddle yourself,' Ruy was telling Jamie firmly. 'Rodriguez will show you how.' As he spoke his eyes swept Davina's trim form in her jeans and the thin tee-shirt she had put on before breakfast. The thin fabric had shrunk a little with numerous washings and clung seductively to the soft curves of her breasts, outlining their tender peaks, and it was on these that Ruy's eyes lingered longest. Heat coursed through her, turning her legs to boneless agony, an ache in the pit of her stomach that made her colour up afresh as she was forced to accept the extent of her desire. Were Ruy even to attempt to touch her at this moment she knew she could not endure it without betraying her love. With a small cry she turned on her heel, desperate to seek the sanctuary of her bedroom.

She was lying on the bed staring at the ceiling when the door was suddenly thrust open and Ruy came in. His unexpected presence brought her bolt upright on the bed, her eyes widening with mingled fear and uncertainty.

'Dreaming of your lover?' Ruy asked sardonically. 'Imagining how it would feel to have his hands upon your body . . . is that why you dressed in such a revealing fashion? *Por Dios*,' he muttered, coming towards her, 'if it is the feel of a man's hands you long for so much that you must seek solitude up here to dream of it, then you shall have it. My hands at least are not crippled.'

Davina moved, but not quickly enough. She could see the stretch fabric of Ruy's cotton knit shirt tautening over the solid muscle of his back as he leaned towards her, his hands fastening on her arms and holding her helpless as they tightened into steel bands whose touch seemed to burn into her very bones.

'No . . .' The small word was a taut protest, cried instinctively as she saw the look on his face; reinforced by a frightened glance upwards from beneath eyelashes which fluttered betrayingly as his warm breath fanned her skin.

'No? You seem to have a habit of saying that word when you mean "yes",' Ruy taunted softly, pulling her off the bed with a strength she found it impossible to deny.

Half lying and half sitting across his lap, with one arm encircling her like a steel brace, she couldn't move, and was forced to endure Ruy's leisurely inspection of her sparkling eyes and flushed cheeks before it moved upwards, lingering on the betraying tremble of her parted lips and lower still to where her breasts strained against the thin tee-shirt, as though mutely imploring his possession.

'Is this that you dreamed of Carlos doing?' he murmured softly, as his tongue moistly caressed her throat, making her shake with the effort of not betraying how much the sensual movement aroused her; how much she longed to unfasten the buttons of his shirt and slide her hands inside it. She looked downwards, not daring to close her eyes in case blotting out their surroundings made her even more vulnerable to the desire storming through her, but that too was a mistake because it brought into her line of vision the dark brown vee of flesh exposed by the neck of his shirt, the crisp tangle of hairs curling darkly there making her stomach somersault weakeningly as she remembered the provocative scrape of the rough hair against the smoothness of her breasts.

'Or this . . .' Ruy suggested, still in the same soft voice, driving her mindless with pleasure as his free hand slid under her shirt to unclip her bra and close over her breast while his tongue outlined the vee-shaped neckline of her shirt, making her shudder with the pleasure it evoked.

Against her will her arms lifted, her fingers curling into the dark hair, revelling in the feel of it as she strained instinctively against him, longing for closer contact with his body.

'Or perhaps this,' Ruy continued, deliberately heightening her torment as his thumb stroked leisurely over her now hard nipple and his tongue lightly traced the outline of her lips until they parted in a harsh moan of surrender, her clasped hands tugging his head downwards so that she could prolong the contact. She made a small sound in her throat, a combination of longing and despair, and as though he too were not unaffected by their proximity Ruy's mouth at last closed demandingly on hers, surprising her with its sensual intensity where she had expected harshness. Her lips parted on a sigh as gladly she abandoned herself to the magic of Ruy's touch, revelling in the heated caress of his hands against her skin, and aching with the need to prolong it.

'So . . .' he released her almost gently, his lips lingering for a tormenting moment before they were withdrawn. 'You see, Davina, there is no need to dream all alone of a lover's caresses. Any man, even a man such as I, can offer appeasement.'

While she was still trying to recover from the agony of the wound he had just inflicted, he continued in the same soft voice, 'And now we shall go downstairs. No ...' he commanded when she slid from his knee and started to straighten her clothing, 'I want Carlos to see you exactly as you are, *querida*. He is a man of much imagination. He won't be required to tax himself unduly to know what has happened. Your skin is pale and bruises easily,' he added significantly, glancing at the mauve shadows already forming on her arms where he had grasped them. 'Now, we shall go downstairs, together, with your lips still swollen from my kisses and your body aroused by my lovemaking ...'

A lift had been installed in the hacienda to make it easy for Ruy to go up and down stairs alone, and as she stood in trembling fury at his side Davina could hardly believe that she had actually heard him correctly. She knew now beyond any shadow of a doubt that he had deliberately come upstairs to seek her out, to make sure that he destroyed what he thought was a love affair between herself and Carlos. The lift came swiftly to a halt, and without stopping to think, driven only by a blind need to punish him as he had punished her, she said huskily:

'Carlos is not like you, Ruy. He's compassionate ... understanding. Knowing that you have ... touched me will not destroy what he feels for me.' And with her head held high she walked from the lift, refusing to look back. It was true, after all. Carlos would understand, but not for the reasons Ruy thought!

Carlos left the hacienda shortly before lunch for the drive to Ronda. He never ate before a fight, he told Davina when she exclaimed that he would miss lunch. He had given them tickets for some of the best seats, and had insisted that they come to his dressing room after the *corrida* was over.

'You are chancing fate, my friend,' was Ruy's only comment. 'I thought you never talk of "afterwards".'

'Perhaps not, in the past,' Carlos agreed with a secret smile for Davina, 'but then I did not have what I now have to look forward to. You will pray for me, *querida*?' he asked Davina softly, raising her fingers to his lips and lingering over the kiss he pressed to them.

'Yes . . .'

'*Bien.*' He turned her hand over and deposited a warm kiss in the palm, closing her fingers over it before releasing her. 'A small keepsake which I shall ask that you return, if I am successful.'

Greatly daring, Davina managed a smile. 'Then I shall have to pray doubly hard that you *are* successful.'

The expression in Carlos' eyes spoke—and promised—volumes, and so did that in Ruy's, only of a very different order!

Obeying some instinct which was only now asserting itself, Davina chose one of her prettiest dresses to change into, white silk chiffon overprinted with flowers in delicate lilacs and mauves. It had long sleeves and a wraparound skirt which left a seductive glimpse of long slender legs as she moved, the vee neckline drawing subtle attention to the swelling thrust of her breasts. High-heeled sandals in matching lavender kid and a hat to match the dress, trimmed with white ribbon, completed the outfit.

She knew that she had chosen well, when Ruy entered their bedroom and stiffened antagonistically.

'So . . . For Jamie and me jeans are good enough, but for Carlos you flaunt your femininity in a parody of innocence that would be laughable if it were not so grotesque. And do not think he will be deceived. Carlos is an astute Spaniard beneath that playboy exterior. His wife, when he takes one, will be pure and docile; until then it pleases him to amuse himself with *rameras* . . . coquettes,' he explained insultingly when Davina looked blankly at him. 'Women who exchange their virtue for tawdry trappings. Women such as you, *mi querida.*'

He said the last words with such savagery that Davina shrank under them, unable to force past her tight throat a single word in her own defence. Half blinded by tears, she stumbled from the room, busying herself with dressing Jamie until she had full control of herself again.

'Mummy cried,' the little boy told Ruy chattily when they were all assembled downstairs, much to Davina's dismay. 'But I kissed her all better, didn't I?'

Davina nodded, thinking in her heart that it was kisses of a far different sort she needed to soothe her lacerated heart. Even so, she could not prevent herself from glancing beneath her lashes at Ruy to see how he had received Jamie's innocent confidences.

His head was tilted to one side as he regarded the little boy. The white silk shirt against the tanned flesh of his throat emphasised his vigorous maleness. He was wearing dark trousers, the fabric clinging firmly to the muscled width of his thighs. An aching sensation began to spread through her lower limbs and she could not

believe that he could not rise from his chair and walk.
He looked so alive, so vital; she wouldn't accept that
he was chained to that chair for the rest of his life.
Something not unlike hysteria rose up inside her and
she had to fight to stop herself from dragging him out
of the chair and forcing him to walk. Only yesterday,
in the fierce heat of his anger, he had seemed to drag
himself upwards, the movement almost imperceptible.
Was rage the key which would turn the lock and free
his paralysed limbs? If so she knew that she could
gladly incite him to the point of murder, were she sure
that it would have the desired effect.

Now, looking at him, lean and dangerous like a pan-
ther at his ease, the firm lips softening as he listened to
Jamie, Davina had an irresistible urge to go to him
and beg him to love her.

Fortunately, before it completely overpowered her
Rodriguez arrived to announce that the car was outside.

Once again Ruy drove, Rodriguez giving Davina a
warm smile as he helped her into the front passenger
seat. As she turned her head to make sure that Jamie
was comfortable she glimpsed again a look of bitter
frustration on Ruy's face. Was he thinking that she
should have been Carmelita? That Jamie should have
been his and Carmelita's child?

The tickets Carlos had given them admitted them to
the very best seats—'sombra' it said on them, which as
his manager explained as he met them at the gate,
meant in the shade. Carlos' manager was a small plump
man with coal black eyes and a small moustache, who
never seemed to stop talking. He rather reminded
Davina of a character out of *Carmen*, but she blessed
Carlos for his thoughtfulness in sending him to them

as she saw how quickly the seats filled up, and how tactfully arranged their seats were, at the end of a row with ample room for Ruy's chair.

Señor Bonares had even thought to provide them with *almohadillas*, comfortable cushions to place on the wooden seats.

Ronda's bullring was among the oldest in Spain, Davina was told with pride, as Señor Bonares took a seat next to her.

'Don Carlos has asked that I explain everything to you,' he told her with a smile. 'And so, Condesa, you must consider me entirely at your service.'

Despite his somewhat comic opera appearance the Señor proved to be an excellent teacher. As a hush fell on the auditorium he directed Davina's eyes towards the President, in his box above them.

He made a sign, incomprehensible to Davina, but seemingly quite clear to everyone else, because the hush took on a tense expectancy, suddenly splintered by the strains of the *pasadoble*, as a procession advanced across the clean sand. In a muted whisper Señor Bonares explained to Davina that the two men leading the procession were *alguacillos*, or constables. They rode on horseback dressed in fantastic medieval costume. They took no part in the *corrida* itself, the Señor added; their appearance was merely a tradition.

Behind the *alguacillos* came the matadors; three of them abreast, all wearing their *trajes de luces*, the so aptly named 'suits of lights'—the most spectacular male dress in the world—the cloth coruscated with shimmering silver and gold and purple. In an aside Señor Bonares informed her that each suit weighed upwards of twenty-five pounds, and she hid a small smile as he pointed Carlos out to her proudly, commenting with a beaming smile, '*Esto muy hombre, si?*'

To the rear of the matadors were their assistants, and behind them again came the picadors on horseback, the sun glinting on their metal leg guards, and finally the *monosabios*, the 'wise monkeys', as the ring servants were called, and the mules, whose purpose, Davina was told, was to remove the carcases of the bulls.

She shuddered a little at that, the words bringing home to her that she was here to witness the death. The other spectators seemed to be stilled by the same knowledge, because the crowd was momentarily silent. The procession disappeared into the *callejon* running alongside the ring.

Again the President's handkerchief fluttered in the afternoon stillness, and to the sound of drums and bugles the first bull entered the ring.

'He is small and timid,' Señor Bonares commented disparagingly, leaning behind Davina to say something to Ruy, who was holding Jamie on his knee so that the little boy could get a better view. 'The Conde agrees with me,' he announced, turning back to her. 'We shall not see much sport from this one.'

What he said proved to be true. The bull, to Davina's secret sympathy, was despatched well within the allotted fifteen minutes and the young *novillado* received a smattering of cheers from the crowd.

'The *novillados* merely whet their appetite,' Señor Bonares told her. 'It is Carlos they have come to see.'

This proved to be true. Carlos was the last matador of the afternoon. He came into the ring proudly at the President's command and bowed first to him, and then, quite deliberately, to Davina. While the crowd roared its appreciation Davina blushed, and caught Carlos' grin as he observed her embarrassmemt.

The bull was released. His name, announced over the loudspeakers, was 'Viento Fuerte', or 'Strong Wind', as Señor Bonares translated for her, and he weighed five hundred and forty kilos, slightly over half a ton.

Davina's throat was dry during the opening stages of the *corrida*. Although the sand had been freshly raked, the smell of blood hung sickeningly upon the air, mingling with the dry heat and the tense expectancy of the crowd to create an atmosphere which she had never experienced before, but which she felt sure must be the closest modern equivalent to that prevailing in the ancient Roman arenas.

The picadors were placing their darts with skilled precision, and Davina averted her eyes in horror as the wicked horns grazed past one pony's withers.

'Don't worry about it,' Ruy advised her drily. 'The pony is well protected by his *peto*. You are too squeamish.'

The picadors withdrew; Carlos advanced, placing the *banderillas* expertly and drawing a cheer from the crowd. They did not like it when the matador wasted time at this stage, Señor Bonares confided to her. 'Carlos was lucky today, he had drawn a bull *muy bravo*.'

Davina shuddered. The animal was pawing the sand, now streaked rusty red with its blood. The small eyes gleamed and the dark head lowered. . . .

'*Por Dios . . . magnifico!*' she heard Señor Bonares exclaim reverently as Carlos swung his cape over his head in a spectacular swirl and the crowd roared fresh approval.

'An *afarolado*,' the Señor breathed, 'the lighthouse.

See how the bull just scrapes past him. *Magnifico!*'

Silence descended yet again. Carlos made several more passes, each one seemingly more dangerous than the last. 'See with what *cargar la suerte* Carlos controls the bull,' her instructor commanded her. 'He has style, and the bull, he is a good one.'

The taut expectancy, the smell of blood mingling with the hot air, combined to make Davina feel dizzy. The bull charged again, suddenly swerving and almost catching Carlos off guard. The tip of the animal's horn grazed his suit, tearing it with a sound which could be clearly heard, and exposing his flesh. The nausea rose inside her. This was how Ruy had been torn, how his flesh had been savaged ... The crowd went wild, shouting out and applauding, and Carlos bowed to them audaciously before turning to face the bull once more.

The scene reminded Davina unbearably of Hemingway's *Death in the Afternoon*; the same atmosphere pervaded the arena. She saw the bull charging on Carlos and covered her eyes, not daring to look. The crowd cheered themselves hoarse, and Señor Bonares shouted excitedly, '*Por Dios*, that was *perfecto*! See, Condesa, the sword is in ... It is over, the bull is vanquished!'

The President made an announcement in Spanish and the crowd roared full-throated approval. Feeling sick and dizzy, Davina watched the mules, gaily caparisoned in green and gold, dragging the huge carcase away.

'Carlos has been awarded both ears and the tail,' Señor Bonares told her. 'It is good to kill the bull like that with one stroke.'

Davina nodded. Jamie was watching round-eyed

with wonder. The paganness of the scene seemed to have escaped the little boy and he was sitting as enthralled as though he had been watching a favourite television programme.

Children saw death so differently, Davina thought, having no conception of what it really was.

'Condesa. Condesa!' Señor Bonares' urgent whisper focused her attention upon him. He was gesturing to her with barely concealed excitement. 'See, Carlos wishes to present you with the ears.'

True enough! Davina saw a grinning Carlos coming towards her through a hail of shoes, handbags, hats, flowers, chocolates and sundry other items which the spectators were throwing at him in recognition of his skill.

Sickness welled up inside her. She tried to speak, to show the appreciation she realised was expected, but the words would not come; the world whirled round her in a coloured kaleidoscope through which all she could hear was Ruy's coolly firm voice saying sardonically, 'You forget, Carlos, my wife is English and not used to such expression of love. Cool English violets need careful handling lest they are crushed and spoiled.'

'Forgive me, *pequeña*,' she heard Carlos apologise. 'I had forgotten. Bonares, bring them all to my dressing room. After this afternoon I feel like celebrating. I shall take you to a restaurant where the food will make you forget everything and think only that you are in heaven,' he promised Davina as he strode off to the accompaniment of ecstatic cheers from the crowd.

'Why did Carlos want to give Mummy those ears?' Jamie enquired, puzzled.

'It is a sign of appreciation . . . a great honour which

does not come the way of many women,' Ruy explained
tongue in cheek, his eyes sliding to Davina's pale face.
'Although perhaps in Carlos' case the latter statement
is not strictly true,' he added unkindly. 'I believe it is
a favourite practice of his to dedicate to his latest mistress the strongest bull. A Freudian practice, would
you not say, *amada*?'

Davina hated it when he used words meant to be
spoken with love in that coldly mocking tone.

'No more Freudian than your behaviour,' she felt
compelled to point out, while Señor Bonares was still
fussily engaged in arranging for them to go down to
Carlos' dressing room.

'So impatient to reach your lover,' Ruy sneered as
she stood up to follow the Spaniard. 'I am surprised
you did not beg him to possess you physically on the
sand where he killed his bull. Come, surely you are
not going to pretend that there aren't women who find
increased sexual enjoyment from that sort of thing, or
that you are one of them . . . I was watching you,' he
told her savagely. 'You were damn near close to faint-
ing with wanting him . . . I am well aware of the effect
the *corrida* can have upon those not brought up in its
traditions, *querida*—and so, I can guarantee, is Carlos.
No doubt he is expecting a warm reception from you
later on and . . .'

'Stop it!' Davina pleaded, covering her ears, and glad
that Jamie had gone on ahead with Señor Bonares.
'How can you say such things to me?' she asked sickly.
'None of it is true.'

But Ruy wasn't listening. He was propelling his
chair away from her without even bothering to glance
over his shoulder to see if she was following.

Crushed and battered by the crowd, she lost sight of

him scores of times as she tried to hurry after him, panic setting in when at one point she thought herself lost altogether, and in danger of being crushed by the crowds.

'*Idiota!*' Ruy abused her as he suddenly materialised at her side grasping her wrist and almost pulling her through the milling crowd.

Carlos' dressing room was full of flowers and gifts which had been sent to him by spectators. He greeted them with a smile. He had not yet changed and was sitting in his sweat-soaked shirt, his jacket thrown carelessly on a chair, from which he removed it to offer the seat to Davina.

She sank down on to it gratefully, caught off guard when Carlos suddenly slipped an arm round her waist and tilted her chin with hard fingers.

'Have you forgotten so quickly, *querida*?' he asked her huskily. 'You have not yet returned my token.'

Enlightenment dawned. He was referring to that kiss he had given her at the hacienda. She smiled uncertainly. Here in the confines of the small dressing room he seemed different, highly charged and somehow a stranger. Excitement glittered in his eyes, and Davina realised with a sense of shock that she had aroused him.

'If you will not give me my reward freely, I shall have to take it by force,' he told her in a low voice, bending his head to capture her lips and part them expertly.

Her hand went instinctively to his shoulder to push him away, but someone else beat her to it.

'*Bastante!*' Ruy grated. 'You forget yourself, Carlos, or is it that you think my infirmity gives you license to dishonour me without fear of reprisals?'

'A kiss ... you, who have so much, begrudge me that?' Carlos countered, once more the teasing young man Davina remembered and liked. 'You make too much of it, *amigo*. Come, I shall take you all out to dinner as a recompense, *si*?'

The meal was not a happy one. In spite of all Carlos' endeavours to lighten it a heavy, threatening tension seemed to infuse the air around them, rather like the oppressive calm before a fierce storm.

Davina could only pick at her food. She had noticed on the menu *filete de toro*, and seeing it had immediately robbed her of what scant appetite she had had.

Carlos was not to return to the hacienda with them. He was dining later with his manager, he explained, and would stay the night with him. As he bent to open the Mercedes' door for Davina he whispered contritely,

'Forgive me, *querida*, I think I have awakened the slumbering tiger in Ruy, and you will have to pay the penalty of my foolhardiness. I meant only to tweak his tail,' he confided ruefully, 'but I had forgotten that today I would be drinking the blood of the bull, and that it makes men foolishly over-confident. I shall visit the hacienda again before I leave Ronda.'

'To make sure I'm all in one piece?' Davina asked ruefully, allowing him to kiss her lightly on the cheek.

Not once during the drive back did Ruy speak to her. He seemed to have retreated behind a wall of icy hauteur, his expression on the rare occasions when he chanced to glance at her contemptuous to the point of shrivelling her with its arctic distaste.

Jamie was asleep when they reached the hacienda. As she stepped out into the scented warmth of the darkness Davina turned to lift him out of the car. There was no point in waking him up to bath him. She would let him sleep on.

The chirruping of the crickets was the only sound to break the sullen silence that seemed to hang over her like a threatening cloud.

By the time she had put Jamie to bed, the sleepiness which had come over her in the car had gone, and she was wide awake but reluctant to go down to the *sala* and face Ruy.

Feeling restless, she changed into jeans and a tartan shirt, picking up a jacket in case she got cold. An overwhelming desire to see again the scene of Ruy's accident had come over her, as though by seeing it she could find the means to free him from the silken bonds that held him fast. Dr Gonzalas had said that modern medical men did not know how the processes of the subconscious worked, but thinking of voodoo and the spells of witches during the Middle Ages, Davina wondered if there might not, among more primitive civilisations, exist those who could penetrate its secrets, even if the tiny kernel of that knowledge was wrapped in mystery and fear, perhaps even a legacy from civilisations more wise in these matters, like the Egyptians who had known the secret of brain surgery and had the ability to hypnotise their patients to a state where they felt no pain, might still exist.

She stepped out into the darkness, shivering a little as it encompassed her, and stood for a moment on the steps trying to steady the frantic beating of her heart. Her senses, alive to the living silence surrounding her, caught the faint sound of wheels. She glanced back into the hall and saw Ruy bearing down upon her, his expression one of livid fury.

'So . . . You leave my house like a thief in the night. Going where? To your lover?'

His hands gripped her wrists, and for a moment Davina felt real fear. He reversed the chair, dragging her along, refusing to release her aching wrist, his grip so tight that it manacled her to his side like a captive prisoner.

The lift was all in darkness. There was a light inside it, but Ruy did not switch it on. The darkness seemed to press down upon her, smothering her, and Davina was relieved when it eventually came to a stop.

Her relief was shortlived when Ruy threw open their bedroom door and dragged her inside, locking it behind him and throwing the key on to a chair.

'So . . . If your lover comes looking for you, he will have the pleasure of knowing that his tardiness has not deprived you of the caresses your body so plainly craves, even if they are bestowed by hands other than his.'

'Ruy, you don't understand . . .' Davina began, but her protests were ruthlessly silenced by the hotly merciless pressure of his mouth forcing her lips apart and stifling all rational thought. His free hand sought the tender curve of her breast, roughly pushing aside the material and exposing the pale gleam of her skin.

Davina gasped as his mouth descended like that of a predator, determinedly seeking the tenderest flesh. She heard her skirt tear as his mouth and hands grew impatient, and then all rational thought—all will to exist apart from him—was suspended as her bones melted to liquid heat, her body a pliant wand in the arms that held her prisoner. The bed was behind her. Ruy pushed her on to it, pinning her to it with his weight so that she could feel every taut muscle; the sharp

angles of his hips beneath the thin trousers, the hard
flatness of his stomach, the harsh sound of his breathing filling her ears as her jeans were discarded and she
was held fast beneath the merciless scrutiny of eyes the
colour of night as they slid in silent assessment inch by
inch over her body.

When at last his eyes returned to her face they were
both breathing unevenly.

'So you want a lover . . . Then you shall have one,'
Ruy told her softly. 'A lover whose image you will
carry imprinted against your bones until the day you
die. *Por Dios*, I have fought against this,' Davina heard
him mutter, 'tried to play the part of a saint; to remember that desire is not love and should never con-
taminate love's sweet fulfilment. But there is fulfilment
of a darker kind to be found just in looking at you.'

What was he saying? That although he loved
Carmelita he desired *her*? Even though he despised
himself for doing so?

He moved restlessly, cupping her face, a smothered
groan forced past his lips.

Answering desire flooded her, hotly tempestuous
and sweet. She glanced downwards in confusion, not
wanting Ruy to see what was in her eyes. One arm
encircled her, holding her slightly away from him, her
skin pale against the bed. She could see his chest rising
and falling unevenly, the dark material encasing his
thighs straining sensually as he moved closer.

'For tonight forget that there is no love between us,'
Ruy muttered thickly. 'Look at me and know that I
desire you, and can make you desire me, and let that
be enough. I want you, Davina,' he emphasised softly.
'Is it not possible that we can find solace together?'

His words weakened her resistance. If she was

honest with herself this was what she wanted, after all.
To be held in his arms, to know that he desired her
. . . and loved her, a stubborn voice protested, but she
refused to listen to it. Her hands reached towards him
in trembling supplication and encountered the hard
breadth of his shoulders. She heard him mutter
something unintelligible and closed her eyes like a child
trying not to see something unpleasant.

'Undress me, Davina.' The thickly spoken command
unleashed her dammed-up feelings. Her hands moved
slowly over his shirt, unfastening the buttons slowly,
and were pushed aside with an impatient oath as Ruy
completed the task with surer hands before grasping
hers and placing them on the taut warmth of his skin.
In the past shyness and uncertainty had always
tempered her desire, but tonight everything within her
urged her to accept what the gods had so casually given
her. Her eyes delighted in the tanned maleness of Ruy's
body against her own, marvelling at the clean, hard
lines of his body, still that of an athlete despite his
accident. The moonlight touched his scar and she
frowned, running compassionate fingers along its
puckered length. This time Ruy did not demur, his
'Dios, querida, how I long to feel the cool benison of
your lips against my flesh!' freeing her to place their
pink softness to the scar much as she had done before,
but this time she was allowed to linger over each tiny
caress—not merely allowed, but encouraged, her exalt-
ing heart rejoiced.

'Adorada . . . love me,' Ruy begged huskily, drawing
her against his body and removing the tiny briefs which
were all that separated her from the heated intimacy of
his thighs. His rough breathing filled her ears, the
burning pressure of his hands on her body inciting her

to move beneath him in answering response. His skin seemed to be on fire, burning fiercely beneath her palms, his muttered words of love interspersed with the hot kisses tormenting her flesh, urging her senses to clamour for his complete possession even as he withheld from her, as though he wanted to drive them both to the edge of oblivion before granting her body the satisfaction they both craved.

The first time when he had aroused her to the point where nothing mattered but the slow sweet surrender of her body to the domination of his, and then withdrew, Davina had thought it an accident, but when for a second and a third time he taught her body to betray her and brought it into trembling subjugation she knew his actions were no accident—and nor was he unaffected by them. His breathing was a ragged torture to his throat, his skin gleaming silkily with sweat as his lips moved down, over her shoulders to pause and bring shuddering pleasure to her body as his tongue stroked roughly first over one nipple and then the other, filling her with an aching need, which was left unappeased by the warm caress of his hand along her thigh, the soft seduction of his kisses on the quivering warmth of her stomach and lower . . .

His name was torn from her throat on a sob that brought an instantaneous response.

When she trembled uncertainly, wondering if this was just another teasing game, the fierce drive of his body as he slid between her thighs promised her that it was not.

This time was different. This time the aching need deep inside her was quenched by the completeness of a possession which carried her far beyond the barriers of any pleasure she had known before, his mouth muffling her small cries of exhausted pleasure, consuming her with an intensity that left room for nothing else.

'Now you will not dare to leave me again,' Ruy murmured in sleepy satisfaction when they were both at peace again. 'Tonight, *querida*, I have given you the child who will be Jamie's brother or sister. Carlos will not take you now. The state of motherhood is sacrosanct to a Spaniard. He will not take you while your body ripens with my child.'

Davina lay staring into the darkness, tears blurring her eyes. So that was why! So that she would not go to Carlos. If only Ruy knew how remote a possibility that had been! Had he done so he would have been spared the necessity of making love to her. She should have felt bitter, but she couldn't. She loved him. Her hands strayed to her stomach and she was unable to deny the faint thrill of pleasure she experienced at the thought of another child—his child. She glanced at his sleeping body. If only there were some way she could help him!

CHAPTER TEN

DAVINA was up early. She hadn't been able to sleep. Jamie was still in bed. All alone she had wandered on to the patio and received a shy smile from the girl setting the table for breakfast. Accepting a cup of coffee, she drank it slowly, a plan beginning to form in her mind. What she had in mind was dangerous—fatal perhaps—but it was something she had to try.

On the pretext of returning her cup she wandered into the kitchen. Dolores was talking to her husband, and she beamed at Davina. 'Enrique is waiting for the *patrón*. At this time of the day he goes to see the bulls.'

Davina already knew this. She had just gone down to the kitchen to confirm it, but Dolores' comment saved her the necessity of asking outright. As she waited she heard the bell which Enrique confirmed was Ruy's summons to him.

When the manager had gone she sauntered out into the sunshine as casually as she could, her red blouse a vivid scarlet splash in the sunshine. She rarely wore red, and finding this blouse in her case had been quite a stroke of luck.

The bull pens were the centre of industrious activity. The animals' bellows reached Davina well before they came in sight, and her stomach contracted sharply as she saw the first one. Its coat was as black as night—as black as Ruy's hair, its small red eyes glinting wickedly as it tossed its horns. Shrinking, she tried not to look at it. She saw Enrique and Ruy approaching the pens and moved towards an olive tree. If they chanced to see her she could always say that she had merely come out for a stroll.

They didn't. Ruy seemed to be engrossed in something Enrique was telling him, his forehead creased in a frown.

Davina knew that the bulls to be shipped out that morning would be driven across the yard from the pasture to the pens. This, as Carlos had told her only yesterday, was the most dangerous part of the whole proceedings, because for several seconds the bulls were not actually confined, and only the skill of the horses and their riders prevented them from breaking free.

This was where Ruy had had his accident due to the momentary negligence of a young boy. Her palms felt damp, and the fingers she touched to her forehead came away stickily wet. The red blouse seemed to draw the heat; she was sure she could smell again the mingled odours of blood and hot, dry sand, as she had done in the bullring yesterday.

Out of the corner of her eye she saw that Ruy and Enrique had reached the pens. Enrique moved away, shouting a command to the men waiting by the gate to the pasture. It was a manoeuvre they conducted every morning.

Please, God, let it work, Davina prayed as she heard the men shouting to the bulls. Whatever happened, at least Ruy would be safe. And would she? She shuddered as she remembered those wickedly sharp horns and small mean red eyes. A bull marks out a man he will kill, just as a matador marks out his bull, Carlos had told her. Quelling her rising panic, she waited until she could see that the bulls were marshalled in the yard. There were four of them, but she only saw one, the huge black animal she had seen as she walked down.

Like a sleepwalker she started to move towards the yard. Behind her she could hear the sounds of the men getting the bulls on the move; the clatter of horses' hooves on the cobbles, the everyday sounds giving way to cries of concern as someone observed what she was doing.

Ahead of her was Ruy, and she clung on to that thought, her eyes finding and focusing on his face even while her mind blotted out the words he was shouting to her.

She knew he was telling her to go back. There was still time. The safety of the barrier was only three yards behind her; all that was needed to keep her from those razor-sharp horns and the half a ton of bone and muscle which would soon be bearing down upon her.

She had worn the red blouse deliberately, knowing the effect it would have on the bulls. They were between her and the men now; she could hear Enrique angrily chivvying them on to reach her, but she didn't hesitate. Out of the corner of her eye she saw the bulky black shape, but she didn't allow her concentration to waver; didn't allow her eyes to leave Ruy's face. Only when she knew that the bull had seen her, when she sensed from the shocked silence of the men that it was going to charge, did she start to run; not directly for safety but diagonally across the yard, changing direction when she heard the drumming of its hooves.

It was the bull and her now. The men had managed to herd the others away, but this one, this black harbinger of death, was pawing the ground behind her, snorting as he caught the scent of her fear.

'Davina ... This way! Don't run, just walk

slowly . . .' She heard the words and ignored them, knowing that her frantic movements, the vivid splash of scarlet, were enticing the animal to destroy her.

Her heart thumped with dry fear. Behind her she could hear the men; someone was trying to distract the bull, waving a red cloth towards it, but it saw only Davina. In front of her was Ruy, sitting in his chair, his hands gripping the sides in white-faced agony. She had a moment to wonder a little at the agony, where she had expected anger, before her foot slipped on a cobble and she was falling . . . falling . . . If only she were a Minoan girl she might have vaulted to freedom over the bull's horns, was her half-hysterical thought as something gored her thigh, burning into it like red-hot steel, and the waves of pain beat upwards, engulfing her.

Her last thought was that she had failed, for Ruy had not moved, had not been provoked into rising from his chair as she had prayed . . . and she had given up her life for nothing.

It was dark and there was a pain in her leg. She tried to move and winced as it increased in tempo.

'Good, you are awake.'

Dr Gonzales was bending over her, shining a torch into her eyes and making her flinch.

'There is no concussion, that is good,' he said to someone standing behind him. For one wild moment Davina thought it was Ruy, but it couldn't be Ruy. Ruy could not stand. The doctor moved and she recognised the slender body of her mother-in-law, only the Condesa looked different somehow. It was several seconds before Davina realised why. The other woman was crying.

'Oh, Davina, how could you? To take such a risk! Have you no thought for Jamie, for . . .'

'She must rest,' the doctor was saying gently. 'The body has received a bad shock, and the heart also, I think, although I am not the one to mend that.' His eyes seemed to hold a knowledge which was denied to Davina. She had risked so much—everything—and now she had lost.

She was handed a glass and she drank thirstily from it, not realising until too late that it had contained a sleeping potion.

When she awoke again Ruy was in the room sitting next to her in his chair, Jamie perched on his lap.

'Naughty Mummy,' Jamie chided severely when she opened her eyes. 'Not to go near the bulls!'

'What were you trying to do?' Ruy asked evenly. 'Destroy yourself as well as my child?'

He was gone before she could make any retort, leaving her to escape back into sleep where she could ignore the pain in her thigh and that in her heart.

She remained in bed for three days. There was no sign of Ruy; but then why should he bother to come and visit her? she asked herself miserably. The Condesa remained at the hacienda. She came to see Davina every day and they talked together. At least they were drawing closer together, Davina reflected one afternoon when her mother-in-law had left with Jamie to take the little boy for a walk. Dr Gonzales was pleased with her progress. Another day and she would be able to get up, he promised her when he came to visit her. He had made no reference to what she had been doing crossing the yard, which surprised Davina a little, because she had expected him to guess what she had hoped to achieve.

Jamie returned from his walk with the Condesa; Dolores brought up her meal; both women seemed to share an air of suppressed excitement.

Davina was surprised when the Condesa did not offer to join her for dinner. She had been doing so lately, explaining that Ruy was busy. As she ate her omelette Davina heard a car door open, and Dolores' voice raised in excited pleasure. Who was their visitor? she wondered.

A knock on the door startled her. She watched it open and Ruy came in, in his chair. Her accident had achieved what her pleading had not, she thought miserably. They now had separate rooms.

'You are feeling better?'

Her throat closed up with pain. She could scarcely look at him, it hurt so much.

'Yes.'

'That was a foolish thing you did. You could have been killed.'

'Yes.' The word acknowledged the truth of both statements.

'So then why, *amada*, did you do it?'

The soft '*amada*' made her shake like a fragile aspen buffeted by an unkind wind.

'I . . .'

'Yes?' Ruy encouraged.

'I . . .'

To her horror two large tears welled and splashed down on to the hand Ruy had placed on the bed.

'Tears?' His voice was so soft that it was almost her undoing. 'Why, *querida*? Is it true that you love me?' he suddenly demanded arrogantly, changing tack.

When her heart had recovered from the shock she countered, 'Do you think I should do?' Lying down in bed wearing nothing but a scanty silk nightdress was not a good position in which to conduct her defence.

'No. But Carlos seems to think you might.'

Carlos? How could he have betrayed her? She looked

wildly into Ruy's face, trying to see if he was just testing her, but all she could see there was tender amusement, and something else—something she could remember seeing only once before, and that had been the day she had agreed to marry him. Men were selfish and impossible, she railed inwardly. Even loving another woman he derived satisfaction from forcing her to acknowledge her love. His hand captured hers, lifting her fingers to his lips and kissing them individually, his eyes never leaving her face. Her whole body tingled tormentingly; the pain in her thigh was forgotten, but not the pain in her heart.

'Well?' Ruy prodded softly. 'Is it true, do you love me, *adorada*?' Weak tears spilled down over her ashen cheeks on to their still interlocked hands. 'Now you cry! Why, I wonder? You crossed that yard deliberately, didn't you, Davina?' His voice was tender no longer, but angry. She could barely bring herself to look at him.

'I wanted to . . .'

'To what?' he asked softly from the wheelchair. 'To walk with me beneath the moonlight and make love under the orange trees, perhaps?'

Her heart stood still and she refused to look at him.

'*Bien*, and so we shall,' Ruy said huskily, as though unable to trust his self-control any longer, 'but for now you will have to be content with this, light of my heart.'

Her head jerked upwards. She could hardly believe her eyes. Ruy was standing up, leaning over her to lift her from the bed and cradle her in his arms as he sat down upon it.

His lips touched hers and she started to shake, unable to believe that it was not all a dream. Ruy moved away to look into her eyes and smiled wryly.

'Very well, *pequeña*, explanations first and then we

shall make love, but I warn you, they must of necessity be brief.' As he spoke he glanced ruefully at his body, and Davina flushed fiery red as she followed the look and witnessed the evidence of his arousal.

'First my apologies,' Ruy said sombrely. 'For my cruelty; for my grossly insulting behaviour I beg your forgiveness, *querida*. My only defence is that I was jealous . . .' He saw the disbelief in her eyes and laughed harshly.

'Oh yes, it is true. Jealousy is a tame word to describe the hell I have been through, first when you left me, and then through all the long years we were apart, and since then, more recently, the agony I have endured thinking you in love with another—but the blame is not all mine, *adorada*. When I telephoned my mother about your accident she insisted on coming straight to the hacienda. She was on the verge of hysteria. You had restored to me the use of my legs, willingly risked your own life, and she had wronged you badly. You see, *pequeña*, my mother had this idea that I should marry Carmelita. I confess there was a time when I considered it—before I met you. But the moment I set eyes on you I knew there was only one woman I could make my wife; only one woman who could fill the aching emptiness of my life.'

'But I thought you loved Carmelita and had only married me to make her jealous,' Davina interposed.

Ruy's smile was tenderly amused.

'Such an innocent, to think a man—any man—would take such a drastic step to court the attention of another woman! No, I married you because I dared not let you out of my sight in case I lost you. You were so young, so innocent . . . I told myself I would teach you to love me as I loved you.'

'You mean a man of your experience didn't realise that I already did?' Davina marvelled, dizzy with the happiness creeping over her.

'Ah, experience flies out the window when love comes in the door,' Ruy retaliated sagely. 'Between them my mother and Carmelita have caused us much unhappiness. I have had the full story from my mother. How she allowed you to believe I was with Carmelita when you were having our child, when in reality I had been called away to an unavoidable meeting—I drove all night to reach the hospital, only to find you had left and taken the baby with you. I was like a man deranged. You had gone with your lover, Carmelita told me, reinforced by my mother. What could I do? I knew if I went after you I was in danger of killing you. I told myself I would get over you . . .'

'How could you believe Carmelita?' Davina murmured. 'You must have known . . .'

'I knew only that you melted like honey in my arms,' Ruy said simply, 'and that your eyes shone like the hearts of pansies, but your heart was a secret to me and one dared not look closely into lest I discover it barred to me.'

'When all the time it already stood open,' Davina said dreamily.

'When I saw you in the Palacio and realised what my mother had done I wanted to die. The last thing I wanted was for you to pity me. Your presence tormented me. I wanted you so badly I couldn't sleep or eat. I told myself it was the act of a man not worthy of the name to force myself upon you, but yet I couldn't help myself.'

'Oh, Ruy!' Her tremulous mouth was kissed into submission, her arms going round his neck as he strained her against him. 'We have a lot of lost time to make up.'

'And you have a lot of reassuring to do,' Ruy announced mock-severely. 'Carlos called to see you. I think he thought I had deliberately allowed you to risk your life for me. He threatened to beat me into a pulp until I told him that I wasn't a helpless cripple any longer. Then he told me that you loved me. For that I have promised him that he shall be godfather to our next child,' Ruy said. Laughter glinted in his eyes as he waited for her to take up the challenge, but Davina was too happy to take exception.

'You can walk? Oh, Ruy!'

'More tears,' he commented, mock-horrified. 'Yes, I can walk—thanks to you. When you ran from that bull, I was filled with helpless rage. I could do nothing. Your life was in danger and I could do nothing. Then I remembered the gun we keep on hand in case of such emergencies, and the next thing I knew I was on my feet walking towards it. I don't know which of us was most surprised when I shot him—myself or the bull.'

'Oh, Ruy . . .'

'Can you say nothing else! Do you realise what you have cost me? That bull was a valuable animal. You will be required to make due recompense.'

'Very well, as long as I can make payment in kind,' Davina agreed, entering the spirit of the game.

Ruy pretended to consider, his head one one side.

'*Si* . . . just as long as the payment you have in mind can be measured in kisses, and long nights spent in your arms, *querida*. We have much to catch up on. I am taking you away for a short time—a true *luna de miel* this time. I own a villa on Menorca, and we shall go there. Madre will look after Jamie, it is all arranged. All that is required is for you to say yes,' he finished huskily.

'Yes . . .' Davina whispered the word against his

throat, delighting in the sudden clenching of his muscles, the dark colour running up under his skin, as he held her away for a few seconds.

'*Madre de Dios!*' he commented feelingly. 'Is this how you treat a man not long out of hospital?' When she gasped he smiled reassuringly into her face. 'No, nothing is wrong. Doctor Gonzales wanted me to have a full check-up, but I am assured that everything is in order.' A brief smile touched his lips. 'I'm afraid the nurses found me impatient, but they understood when I told them that I was anxious to get back to my wife. That is why I haven't been to see you before . . . That, and because I thought perhaps you had taken such a drastic step to . . .'

'Kill myself and our child,' Davina reminded him with a wan smile.

'*Dios*, forgive me for that,' Ruy groaned. 'No, *querida*, what I really feared, knowing your tender heart, was that you might have tried to free me in order to free yourself. For a moment I was tempted to pretend that I was not healed. Carlos reassured me on that point, as did your face when I came in here tonight. How could you ever think that my life was of any value to me without you in it?'

'Doctor Gonzales said it might work . . .' was all she could think of to say.

'*Dios!* I am sure he said no such thing. He would no more have wanted you to take such a risk than I did. But he has given me some food for thought, I admit. I would not believe him when he told me the paralysis was of the mind. I was too proud to admit that it might, as he said, be a way of pleading with you to return, as though my body knew what my heart refused to admit, that you were too kind, too compassionate to be as I stubbornly kept telling myself you were. And now, *querida*,' he said, with a glint in his eyes that brought the colour to Davina's cheeks, 'I think it is time that I showed you my gratitude with more than words, *si*? What would you prefer?' he teased. 'For us to dance, perhaps, so that you may be assured of how fully recovered I am? Or . . .'

Davina's insistent tugging on his shirt brought his face level with hers. Her lips parted, mutely pleading, but refusing to take any further initiative.

'*Adorada*,' Ruy muttered throatily, closing the small space between them. 'Beloved Davina . . .' She winced involuntarily as the pressure of his hands on her body affected the wound on her thigh. In time the scar would fade, Dr Gonzales had told her kindly. The wound was clean and not very deep, but for now it sometimes ached painfully.

'What is it?'

If she hadn't believed Ruy before, she did now. The look in his eyes melted her heart with tenderness.

She touched her thigh and his eyes followed the betraying movement. '*Si* . . .' he breathed jerkily, tenderly pushing her back on the bed and moving aside the thin silk.

His lips caressed the scarred tissue, and she shuddered in mindless delight.

'Yes, it is a little touch of hell, is it not?' he agreed huskily, taking her in his arms, 'this touch of the one we love against our wounds. Tonight each of us will be balm to the other's heart and soul, *amada*, and you shall greet the morning in my arms—as you shall greet it for the rest of our lives.'

His name was lost beneath his kiss. Happiness flooded her. She was here where she wanted to be, locked safe in the haven of Ruy's protective embrace.

Mills & Boon
Best Seller Romances

The very best of Mills & Boon Romances
brought back for those of you who missed
them when they were first published.
In June
we bring back the following four
great romantic titles.

SOMETHING EXTRA
by Janet Dailey

Jolie didn't really want to settle down at home and marry John Talbot,
whom she liked but didn't love, so she took herself off on a trip to
Louisiana – where she met the decidedly disturbing Steve Cameron.
Wouldn't she have done better to stay at home?

AFFAIR IN VENICE
by Rachel Lindsay

When Erica went to work in Venice she had never dreamed that she
would end up by falling in love with the attractive, immensely rich
Conte Filippo Rosetti. And Filippo's close friend Claudia Medina, it
soon appeared, was going to see to it that it remained only a dream!

VALLEY DEEP, MOUNTAIN HIGH
by Anne Mather

Andrea Connolly was convinced that Axel von Mahlstrom was a
fortune-hunter, and she thought out an effective way of teaching him
a lesson. Unfortunately Axel turned the tables on her in an
unexpected and decidedly disturbing manner . . .

A LESSON IN LOVING
by Margaret Way

Rosslyn was spending the summer vacation at Belyando in Northern
Australia, looking after a rather difficult small child – but soon found
that her real problems were being caused by the child's uncle, Boyd
Ballinger, who announced that he was a bachelor and intended
to remain one!

If you have difficulty in obtaining any of these books through
your local paperback retailer, write to:
Mills & Boon Reader Service
P.O. Box 236, Thornton Road, Croydon, Surrey, CR9 3RU

Romance

Next month's romances from Mills & Boon

Each month, you can choose from a world of variety in romance with Mills & Boon. These are the new titles to look out for next month.

FORGOTTEN LOVER Carole Mortimer
LATE HARVEST Yvonne Whittal
STARTING OVER Lynsey Stevens
BROKEN RHAPSODY Margaret Way
BLIND MAN'S BUFF Victoria Gordon
LESSON IN LOVE Claudia Jameson
MIDNIGHT LOVER Charlotte Lamb
STORM CYCLE Margaret Pargeter
PACIFIC PRETENCE Daphne Clair
WILDFIRE ENCOUNTER Helen Bianchin
THE OTHER BROTHER Jessica Steele
THE MAGNOLIA SIEGE Pamela Pope

Buy them from your usual paperback stockist, or write to: Mills & Boon Reader Service, P.O. Box 236, Thornton Rd, Croydon, Surrey CR9 3RU, England. Readers in South Africa-write to: Mills & Boon Reader Service of Southern Africa, Private Bag X3010, Randburg, 2125

Mills & Boon
the rose of romance

ROMANCE

Variety is the spice of romance

Each month, Mills & Boon publish new romances. New stories about people falling in love. A world of variety in romance – from the best writers in the romantic world. Choose from these titles in June.

DIAMOND CUT DIAMOND Jane Donnelly
RED ROSE FOR LOVE Carole Mortimer
VALLEY OF LAGOONS Kerry Allyne
A GIRL TO LOVE Betty Neels
BITTER-SWEET WATERS Yvonne Whittal
AN OLD PASSION Robyn Donald
WAITING Karen van der Zee
MAKEBELIEVE MARRIAGE Flora Kidd
EDGE OF TEMPTATION Anne Mather
THE CAGED TIGER Penny Jordan
THE WINDS OF HEAVEN Margaret Way
THE SLEEPING FIRE Daphne Clair

On sale where you buy paperbacks. If you require further information or have any difficulty obtaining them, write to: Mills & Boon Reader Service, PO Box 236, Thornton Road, Croydon, Surrey CR9 3RU, England.

Mills & Boon
the rose of romance

How to join in a whole new world of romance

It's very easy to subscribe to the Mills & Boon Reader Service. As a regular reader, you can enjoy a whole range of special benefits. Bargain offers. Big cash savings. Your own free Reader Service newsletter, packed with knitting patterns, recipes, competitions, and exclusive book offers.

We send you the very latest titles each month, postage and packing free – no hidden extra charges. There's absolutely no commitment – you receive books for only as long as you want.

We'll send you details. Simply send the coupon – or drop us a line for details about the Mills & Boon Reader Service Subscription Scheme. Post to: Mills & Boon Reader Service, P.O. Box 236, Thornton Road, Croydon, Surrey CR9 3RU, England. *Please note: READERS IN SOUTH AFRICA please write to: Mills & Boon Reader Service of Southern Africa, Private Bag X3010, Randburg 2125, S. Africa.

Mills & Boon
the rose of romance